swap&
drop
DIET
COOKBOOK

swap& drop DIET COOKBOOK

Reader's Digest Association (Canada) ULC
Montreal • Toronto

Project Staff

EXECUTIVE EDITOR **COURTENAY SMITH**

MANAGER, ENGLISH BOOK EDITORIAL & PROJECT EDITOR **PAMELA JOHNSON**

ASSOCIATE EDITOR **ALISON RAMSEY**

CONTRIBUTING EDITOR **MATTHEW BROWN**

COPY EDITING & PROOFREADING **JENN HARDY & ROBERT RONALD**

SENIOR ART DIRECTOR **ANDRÉE PAYETTE**

BOOK DESIGNERS **ANN DEVOE, OLENA LYTVYN**

CONTRIBUTING DESIGNER **DIANA LEVIN**

PRODUCTION ARTIST **CHRIS A. CANT**

ADMINISTRATOR **LISA PIGEON**

RIGHTS COORDINATOR **PIERRE CHARLEBOIS**

INDEXER **PATRICIA BUCHANAN**

For Best Health Magazine

EDITOR-IN-CHIEF **BONNIE MUNDAY**

ART DIRECTOR **STEPHANIE HAN**

Reader's Digest Association (Canada) ULC

GENERAL MANAGER, CANADA **PHILIPPE CLOUTIER**

The Reader's Digest Association, Inc.

PRESIDENT AND CHIEF EXECUTIVE OFFICER **ROBERT E. GUTH**

GENERAL MANAGER, NORTH AMERICA **MARILYNN JACOBS**

EXECUTIVE VICE PRESIDENT, RDA & PRESIDENT, EUROPE **DAWN ZIER**

CHIEF CONTENT OFFICER, NORTH AMERICA **LIZ VACCARIELLO**

NOTE TO READERS

We pledge that the information and advice inside *Swap & Drop Diet Cookbook* has been checked carefully for accuracy and is supported by leading health experts and up-to-date research. However, each person's health and healing regimens are unique. Even the best information should not be substituted for, or used to alter, medical therapy without your doctor's advice.

Swap & Drop Diet Cookbook is published by *Best Health*, an imprint of Reader's Digest Association (Canada) ULC, 1100 René-Lévesque Blvd. West, Montreal, QC H3B 5H5

ISBN: 978-1-55475-134-1

Library and Archives Canada Cataloguing in Publication
Best Health swap & drop diet : get slim, stay slim / from the editors of Best Health.

ISBN 978-1-55475-134-1
1. Reducing diets--Canada. 2. Weight loss--Canada. I. Title: Best Health swap and drop diet.

RM222.2.B475 2011   613.2'5   C2011-906708-0

PRINTED IN CHINA

Credits:

t - top	tl - top left
c - centre	tr - top right
b - bottom	cl - centre left
l - left	cr - centre right
c - centre	bl - bottom left
r - right	br - bottom right

All photos RDA, except: **5** Geehae Jeong, Hair & Makeup: Mary Luong; **7** Deklofenak/Shutterstock; **14** Monticelllo/Fotolia; **17** Ryan Szulc, food stylist: Claire Stubbs, prop stylist: Madeleine Johari; **18** Brandon Blinkenberg/Shutterstock; **20** Ryan Szulc, food stylist: Noah Witenoff, prop stylist: Madeleine Johari; **22** cl, UltraONEs/iStockphoto; cr, ermingut/iStockphoto; **26** c, Marina Grau/Fotolia; tc, duckman76/Fotolia; **27** background: petekarici/iStock, bl, nikolae/Fotolia; t, Vera Kuttelvaserova; b, Elina Manninen/Fotolia **30** Edward Pond, food stylist: Nicole Young, prop stylist: Genevieve Wiseman; **34** Kuzmin Andrey/Shutterstock; **37** Ariwasabi/Shutterstock **41** Viktar iStockphoto **42** Kryczka/iStockphoto; **47** LuVo/iStockphoto; **64** Photocrea/iStockphoto; **65** Floortje/iStockphoto; **66** tl, photosoup/iStockphoto; bc, cosmin4000/iStockphoto; **69** bl, hlphoto/iStockphoto; **73** alexandrumagurean/iStockphoto; **78** bl, A-S-L/iStockphoto; **80** fesoj/iStockphoto; **82** cl, Fullerene/iStockphoto; **83** br, AntiMartina/iStockphoto; **85** lkphotographers/iStockphoto; Ziva_K /iStockphoto; **86** LordRunar/iStockphoto; **87** James Baigrie/Picture Artist/First Light; **92** bl, Ryan Szulc, food stylist: Noah Witenoff, prop stylist: Madeleine Johari; **99** rolfik /Shutterstock; **100** cl, Ryan Szulc, food stylist: Noah Witenoff, prop stylist: Madeleine Johari; **101** cr, Creativeye99/iStockphoto; **102**, John Cullen, food stylist: Ashley Denton/Judy Inc, prop stylist: Martine Blackhurst; **114-115** John Cullen, food stylist: Ashley Denton/Judy Inc, prop stylist: Martine Blackhurst; **122** tl, LUGO/iStockphoto; **124-125** Ryan Szulc, food stylist: Noah Witenoff, prop stylist: Madeleine Johari; **127** mphillips007/iStockphoto; **129** cr, zkruger/iStockphoto; **130** Elinag/Shutterstock; **131** background: ivanmateev/iStock; bottom left to right: Vadim Kolobanov/Shutterstock; RDA; Palmer Kane LLC/Shutterstock; objectsforall/Shutterstock; Palmer Kane LLC/Shutterstock; Evgeny Karandaev/Shutterstock; **132** Alasdairjames/iStockphoto; **138** foodandmore/Shutterstock; **141** AntonioDiaz/Fotolia; **145** br, Photodisk; **146** Alan Richardson; **147** background: ChuckSchg Photography/iStock; tl, nikolae/Fotolia; t, auryndrikson/Fotolia; cr, Michael Boyny/Stock Food Canada; br, Ryan Szulc/Fotolia; cl, Edward Pond; **148** bl, Photodisk; **152** bl, Photodisk; **153** tr, Photodisk; **154** Tammy Dery; **155** cr, Photodisk; **160** background: lucop/iStockphoto; bl, stargatechris/iStockphoto; bc, VladislavDanilin/iStockphoto; **161** background: bagi1998/iStockphoto, tc, nikolae/Fotolia; lc, Christopher Stevenson **162** Photodisk; **164** tl, oriori/Shutterstock; **165** Photodisk; **167** cr, happykanppy/Shutterstock; **169** Photodisk; **174** tl, Marco Speranza/Shutterstock; **177** cr, Sally Scott/Shutterstock; **178-179** Maya Visnyei, food stylist: Heather Shaw/Judy Inc., prop stylist: Madeleine Johari; **180** tl, Photodisk; b, John Cullen, food stylist: Ashley Denton/Judy Inc., prop stylist: Martine Blackhurst; **181** cr, Photodisk; b, John Cullen, food stylist: Ashley Denton/Judy Inc, prop stylist: Martine Blackhurst; **184** tl, Photodisk; **185** cr, Photodisk; **193** tr, Photodisk; **199** Photodisk; **205** Photodisk; **207** tr, Photodisk; **209** cr, Photodisk; **214** paulbinet/iStockphoto; **217** Alexandr Markin/Shuttestock; **221** cl, Edward Pond,food stylist: Nicole Young, prop stylist: Catherine Doherty; **224-225** Maya Visnyei, food stylist: Claire Subbs, prop stylist: Catherine Doherty; **228** l, Jodi Pudge, food stylist: Nanci Miranda, prop stylist: Lora Branson; **229** b, Ryan Szulc, food stylist: Nanci Miranda, prop stylist: Madeleine Johari; **236** tl, Photodisk; b, Photo courtesy of McNeil Consumer Healthcare, division of Johnson & Johnson Inc.; **240** cl, Photodisk; **241** tr, Photodisk; b, Photo courtesy of McNeil Consumer Healthcare, division of Johnson & Johnson Inc.; **242** tl, Photodisk; b, bamb00x/iStockphoto; **243** Photo courtesy of McNeil Consumer Healthcare, division of Johnson & Johnson Inc.; **246** tl, Michael Alberstat, food stylist: Carl Dudar, prop stylist: Jane Hardin; bl, John Cullen, food stylist: Ashley Denton/Judy Inc, prop stylist: Martine Blackhurst; br, Bryan Szulc, food stylist: Noah Witenoff, prop stylist: Madeleine Jonari; **247** tl, Keller & Keller Photo/stock Food/Maxx Images; br, Courtesy of Food Network Canada; **back cover** iQoncept/Fotolia.

FOREWORD

by Sue Mah, MHSc., RD

Sue Mah is a Registered Dietitian and President of Nutrition Solutions Inc., a company specializing in nutrition communications. She is a pro at deciphering the science of nutrition research into everyday sensible advice to educate, empower, and inspire Canadians to eat better.

Food, nutrition, and health were a part of my life long before I became a Registered Dietitian. My passion for health and wellness was ignited by my love of the delicious food and wholesome meals I ate while growing up. My dad is a Chinese chef, and it was his cooking and philosophy of eating that first taught me about nutrition and balance. Meals were cooked from scratch using the freshest ingredients he could find. Every meal included at least two veggies and a lean protein. Dessert was usually fresh fruit. For family birthdays, Dad went all out with lobster, stir-fried noodles, and homemade strawberry shortcake.

As a nutrition expert and regular contributor to the *Best Health* magazine, I stand by the principles of nutrition and balance. That's why I love the **Swap & Drop Diet Cookbook**. So often, we get caught up in the media hype about the latest diet or weight loss trick. **Swap & Drop** isn't a fad diet or a trick at all! On the contrary, it's a simple and sensible strategy–when you trade in one unhealthy ingredient, meal, or snack for a better one, it adds up over time to a healthier you. The recipes are nutritious, delicious, and balanced. There are no taboo foods, no self-deprivation and definitely no skipping of meals–which are all common diet traps.

In fact, when it comes to food taboos and deprivation, I have two words of advice: ditch them! Like many people I know, I adore chocolate, and I like to serve a sweet treat when entertaining. The **Swap & Drop Diet Cook-**

book contains recipes for chocolate mousse, brownies, and truffles. Sound delicious? They are! For me, it's about balance. I allow myself to enjoy treats without guilt, though not every day. I balance those choices with lower calorie choices throughout each day.

I believe that the best "diet" is the one YOU can stick with for the long run, whether you're trying to lose weight or maintain your current weight. That means forming healthy eating habits that make sense to you and, more importantly, habits that can easily become part of your everyday routine.

One of the most important habits is to eat breakfast every day. Not only does a solid breakfast kick-start your metabolism, but it also plays a role in weight loss and weight management. Research from the National Weight Control Registry, a database of over 10,000 individuals who have lost significant amounts of weight and kept it off, shows that eating breakfast regularly is a key factor in helping keep the weight off.

Get into the habit of eating mindfully too. With our time-crunched schedules, who hasn't eaten in the car or while watching TV? Unfortunately, all of these distractions can lead to mindless eating and overeating. Tune into your internal satiety cues. Eat when you're hungry instead of when you're bored or lonely. Stop eating when you feel full instead of when you feel stuffed. Take time to enjoy your food with all of your senses. Focus on your food's flavour, aroma, colour, and texture. Each recipe in the **Swap & Drop Diet Cookbook** features a beautiful, mouth-watering photo. They'll inspire you to try them all! I really like the flavour swaps and variations. They're fun ways to surprise your taste buds so that you don't get bored.

Finally, make small dietary changes. They add up over time. When my mom was first diagnosed with pre-diabetes a few years ago, she was overwhelmed with all of the changes she needed to make. We took it one small step at a time. First, she cut back on her portion size of white rice. Then, she swapped her regular bread for a high fibre whole-grain bread. And then she started adding an extra serving of veggies at dinner. Now she does all of this without even thinking about it. Her blood sugar levels are under control without medications, and she's lost about 10 pounds.

You too can achieve success, and the **Swap & Drop Diet Cookbook** is the perfect resource. It's filled with easy tips, inspiring ideas, and more than 160 delicious recipes to help you make those small, lasting changes that will help you eat deliciously, be healthy, and feel your best.

WELCOME TO THE COMPANION COOKBOOK TO THE **SWAP & DROP DIET**

If you've purchased this book, we hope it's because you've already started on your **Swap & Drop Diet** journey, and are looking for more delicious **Swap & Drop** recipes! This companion book gives you months of new meals and snacks, tips, and ideas to keep you on track with your healthier way of eating.

If this is your introduction to the **Swap & Drop Diet,** welcome! In this book you'll learn about **Swap & Drop**'s sensible, easy-to-follow way to eat better–and deliciously–while losing weight. You won't find any fad eating or drastic calorie reduction that only undercuts your success in becoming a healthy weight while eating healthfully. It would be helpful, however, to check the meal planner in the **Swap & Drop Diet** book.

The **Swap & Drop Diet** can help you lose weight, but it also helps you maintain a healthy weight. It's a no-diet diet; the word "diet" is used in its broad sense to mean all the things that you eat.

Swapping out fat-laden ingredients and foods, then swapping in flavourful replacements is the core of this diet. Eating sensible portions regularly–and that includes snacks–helps keep extreme hunger at bay, so you don't feel like gorging at mealtime. Enjoying what you eat, eating slowly, and learning to recognize when you're truly hungry and when you're full are all key to weight loss and weight maintenance.

This is how the **Swap & Drop Diet** works: prepare and eat 3 balanced meals, plus snacks, that have a daily total of 1,300 calories to 1,600 calories (for those who exercise regularly). Calories from fat are limited to 35 percent max, with saturated fats accounting for no more than 10 percent. Each day, consume at least 25 grams of fibre. And get walking to keep the weight off! (For complete guidance, and further information and inspiration, please refer back to our companion book, **Swap & Drop Diet**.)

This is how the **Swap & Drop Diet Cookbook** works: All the recipes are healthful, scrumptious meals and snacks suited to the Diet. Each recipe has a highly visible calorie count at the top of the page; you can create your own daily or weekly meal plans by combining ones that add up to your goal.

The **Swap & Drop Diet** isn't just for today, tomorrow, or next week. It's the basis of healthy eating habits to last a lifetime. That means the recipes have to taste fantastic–and they really do. We know you're going to love them. Enjoy!

CALORIES PER DAY TO MAINTAIN YOUR WEIGHT

FEMALE ADULTS (CALORIES PER DAY)

Age	Level of daily activity		
	Sedentary	Low Active	Active
19-30	1,900	2,100	2,350
31-50	1,800	2,000	2,250
51-70	1,650	1,850	2,100
71 +	1,550	1,750	2,000

MALE ADULTS (CALORIES PER DAY)

Age	Level of daily activity		
	Sedentary	Low Active	Active
19-30	2,500	2,700	3,000
31-50	2,350	2,600	2,900
51-70	2,150	2,350	2,650
71 +	2,000	2,200	2,500

■ **Sedentary** *This describes people who are sitting most of the day, and who do not exercise or walk any distance to work or during their leisure time.*
■ **Low Active** *This describes people who do some small activity daily (mow the lawn, shovel snow, walk a few blocks), and also enjoy doing non-sedentary acitivities in their leisure time.*
■ **Active** *This describes people who do moderate to vigorous activity for 2 ½ hours each week.*

SOURCE: Health Canada, Canada's Food Guide

CONTENTS

PART 1 ■ breakfasts

PART 2 ■ light fare

PART 3 ▦ main meals

PART 4 ■ sweeties

1

BREAKFASTS

1 Breakfasts Make it a good morning every morning with a healthy start to the day

Get the day off on the right foot with a decision to eat well, and deliciously, by having a good-for-you, yet tantalizingly tasty, breakfast. Take some advice on maximizing the benefits of this important meal using tips for everyday breakfasts on pages 16 and 17. Or dive directly into our bundle of recipes that deliver big taste for leisurely meals while keeping calories in check.

Breakfast is a wonderful opportunity to incorporate fresh fruit into your diet, which gives you a double benefit: your mouth longs to rehydrate after sleep and what better way than with juicy fruits? Fresh fruit also delivers what juices alone can't: fibre. Fibre-rich foods are a

Swap & Drop *staple because of medical proof that they improve your life. How? Scientific research shows that a diet rich in fibre can be helpful in sustaining long-term weight loss, prevent diabetes, keep cholesterol in check, and reduce your risk of cancer.*

Before you turn the page and skip another breakfast, ask yourself this: Are you a mid-morning grouch? Here's another reason to take the time to eat right early in the day:

Pilot studies have shown that eating fruit and whole-grain foods at breakfast not only helps control appetite and insulin resistance, it also improves your mood. So, dish it up and smile!

Simple changes shed pounds

And here's one simple truth: People who eat breakfast are less likely to be obese

"Small changes made daily that fit easily into your schedule are a painless way to cut calories. All it takes is one or two better choices to reach the 500 calories a day that trims the scales by one pound a week."

—*Swap & Drop Diet*

Plenty of dieters forgo breakfast, figuring they'll end up eating fewer calories that way–when in fact it's the other way around. People who skip breakfast end up consuming more calories during the day than those who eat a proper breakfast.

Getting the day off to a good start eases mid-morning hunger pangs and gives you a nutritional boost of lasting value.

So don't forget to eat breakfast, and make it a smart one. A good start (even on busy days) includes a sizable portion of filling fibre. Follow three basic breakfast rules: eat fruit (juice has more calories and little fibre), eat protein, and choose whole-grain breads and high-fibre cereals.

We've rounded up some more easy changes you can make early in the day, when your resolve is most firm–pick a few and the scale will start to shift in the right direction. Swap your daily frappuccino for a coffee and you're about halfway to cutting 500 calories a day.

Remember, though, to give yourself time to adjust to any food swap, says Robin Anderson, a registered dietitian with Revive Wellness, a coalition of health practitioners in Edmonton. The more salt, fat, and sugar, the more addictive a food is. So you need to give your taste buds a chance to adapt to any shift.

Along with eating a protein, try these healthy swaps

Choose toast. Replace a bagel (354 calories) or store-bought blueberry muffin (440 calories) with 2 slices of whole-wheat toast (164 calories). Skip the butter, but you can add a tablespoon (15 mL) of honey (64 calories) or ½ cup (125 mL) of fat-free cottage cheese (90 calories). Calorie savings: up to 276. Do this once a week to slash more than 14,300 calories a year–that's more than 4 pounds.

Eat, don't drink, your fruit. An orange, at about 60 calories, is half that of a cup of juice, but there's more good news: an orange has 3.3 grams of fibre, the juice only 0.4 grams.

soy (unsweetened)
80 calories
4 g fat (0.5 g saturated fat)
7 g protein

2% 130 calories
5 g fat (3 g saturated fat)
9 g protein

rice (unsweetened)
110 calories
1 g fat (0.3 g saturated fat)
2 g protein

almond (unsweetened)
30 calories
2 g fat (0.2 g saturated fat)
1 g protein

skim 90 calories
0.5 g fat (0 g saturated fat)
8 g protein

1% 100 calories
2.5 g fat (1.5 g saturated fat)
9 g protein

The same, but different: All these glasses contain a 1-cup (250-mL) portion of milk or other beverage; all deliver the same amount—about 30%—of your daily calcium requirement.

Bake your own. At 400 calories or more, hefty store-bought muffins are your enemy. Make regular-sized ones yourself, or try a slice of banana bread that, at 228 calories, saves you 172. Make the swap once a week to cut out 8,944 calories a year, equalling 2 ½ pounds.

Buy sugar-free jam. Using 2 tablespoons (30 mL) is just 20 calories, compared with 100 calories in traditional jam.

Swap your milk. One cup of whole milk comes in at 146 calories and 7.9 g of fat, while 1% racks up 100 calories and 2.5 g of fat. Or try fortified soy beverage (80 calories, 4 g fat) or, for your best swap option, develop a taste for unsweetened almond beverage (30 calories, 2 g fat). Savings: up to 116 calories and 3.9 g of fat. Do this daily for an astonishing loss of 41,296 calories, nearly 12 pounds.

Whip margarine. Use a hand blender to whip trans-fat-free, soft-tub margarine. By incorporating air, you'll use less.

Make Greek-style yogurt. This velvety yogurt has more protein than regular, so you feel fuller longer. Just strain plain yogurt (gelatin/preservative-free) through cheesecloth stretched over a bowl, secured with an elastic band. Let sit for a few hours in the fridge; discard liquid.

Even more swaps

Skip a yolk. Nix just 1 yolk from 2-egg meals like omelettes to cut both calories and fat. A whole egg weighs in with 75 calories and 5 g of fat; the white has just 16 calories and no fat. Calorie savings: 59. Make this change once a week to drop 3,068 calories a year, nearly a pound.

Make your own breakfast sandwich. Use a whole-wheat English muffin, microwave poach an egg, then add a slice each of tomato and fat-free cheese. Calorie savings: about 500. Swap this in once a week for a 26,000-calorie savings, about 7.5 pounds.

Eggheads know this

○ **Omega-3 eggs** are from hens fed a diet high in polyunsaturated omega-3 fatty acids essential to human growth. Flaxseed or fish oil is added to feed.

○ **Organic eggs** are from hens whose feed is free of herbicides, pesticides, fungicides, and preservatives. They have more vitamin A, D, and E and taste richer.

○ **Free-range** eggs are from hens that roam inside and out, weather permitting.

○ **Free-run** hens are housed in barns, with nests, perches and more space to scratch, peck, and stretch their wings. Unlike bread, brown and white eggs are equally nutritious.

PECAN WAFFLES WITH MAPLE, PEAR & BLACKBERRY SAUCE

SERVES 4

Crisp on the outside, tender on the inside, waffles are as popular around the world come Sunday morning as they are in PEI, Ontario, or Alberta. This version sounds fancy, but it's actually simple and delicious.

360 calories per serving

⅔ cup	flour	150 mL
½ tsp	ground cinnamon	2 mL
1 tsp	baking powder	5 mL
1 tbsp	sugar	15 mL
	1 large egg, separated	
1 cup	fat-free milk	250 mL
2 tbsp	margarine, melted	30 mL
2 tbsp	pecans, finely chopped	30 mL
	SAUCE	
	1 large, ripe dessert pear	
4 tbsp	maple syrup	60 mL
½ cup	pecan halves	125 mL
½ cup	blackberries	125 mL

1 First, make the maple and fruit sauce. Cut the pear lengthwise into quarters and cut out the core, then cut the pear into fine dice. Put into a small heavy saucepan and add the maple syrup. Warm gently, then remove the pan from the heat. Stir in the pecan halves and the blackberries. Set aside while making the waffles.

2 Heat and lightly grease the waffle iron or maker according to the manufacturer's instructions.

3 Meanwhile, make the waffle batter. Sift the flour, cinnamon, baking powder, and sugar into a medium mixing bowl. Make a well in the centre, and add the egg yolk and milk to the well. Gently whisk the egg yolk and milk together, then gradually whisk in the flour to make a thick, smooth batter. Whisk in the melted margarine, then stir in the finely chopped pecans.

4 Whisk the egg white in a separate bowl until stiff. Pile it on top of the batter and, using a large metal spoon, fold it in gently.

5 Spoon a small ladleful (3 to 4 tbsp/45 to 60 mL) of batter into the centre of the hot waffle iron or maker, then close the lid tightly. After about 2 or 3 minutes, open the waffle iron. The waffle should be golden brown on both sides and should come away easily from the iron.

6 Lift the cooked waffle from the iron using a butter knife, and keep warm while cooking the rest of the waffles.

7 Just before all the waffles are ready, gently warm the fruit sauce, then pour into a sauceboat or serving bowl. Serve with the warm waffles.

PER SERVING: 8 g protein, 15 g total fat, 2 g saturated fat, 257 mg cholesterol, 51 g carbohydrates, 4 g fibre.

HOME SWEET HOME
Authentic maple syrup contains healthy amounts of **zinc**.

SWAP IT OUT!

● ● ● **Parmesan waffles**: Omit the cinnamon, sugar, and pecans from the batter. Instead, sift the flour with a good pinch each of black pepper and cayenne pepper, and salt to taste. Add 2 tbsp (20 mL) freshly grated Parmesan cheese before folding in the egg white. Omit the fruit sauce.

● ● ● Use walnuts instead of pecans, and either maple syrup or clear honey in the sauce.

ASPARAGUS & TOMATO OMELETTE

SERVES 4

Endlessly variable, the simple omelette can reflect any season you wish. This one sings of spring, when asparagus is at its most tender.

4 tsp	olive oil, divided	20 mL
	1 small onion, finely chopped	
	1 clove garlic, minced	
	12 cherry tomatoes, halved	
	8 asparagus spears, trimmed and cut in thirds	
	Small handful basil, chopped	
	8 medium eggs	
¼ cup	crumbled feta cheese	60 mL
	Mixed olives (optional)	

214 calories per serving

SWAP IT OUT!

● ● ● **A flat omelette is a versatile dish** and there are many variables you can try. Other fillings: zucchini and diced ham, marinated artichokes and pitted olives, cooked chicken and grated cheese. Serve with a green salad.

1 Set oven to warm. Pour 2 tsp (10 mL) oil into a medium frying pan over medium heat; add onion and sauté until softened, about 5 minutes. Add garlic, tomatoes, and asparagus; simmer about 5 minutes. Toss in basil; remove from heat.

2 Meanwhile, in a large bowl, whisk eggs with 1 tbsp (15 mL) cold water. In a large frying pan, heat 1 tsp (5 mL) oil over medium heat. Pour in half the beaten eggs. Lift edges gently inward as eggs set, allowing the uncooked portion to flow underneath.

3 When the top is set and underside is browned, spoon half of the asparagus/tomato mixture onto one half, sprinkle with half the feta, then use a spatula to flip the omelette's other half over top.

4 Transfer to an ovenproof dish and place in oven. Repeat with remaining oil, eggs and filling. Place half an omelette on each of 4 plates. Garnish with basil.

PER SERVING: 14 g protein, 15 g total fat, 5 g saturated fat, 381 mg cholesterol, 6 g carbohydrates, 2 g fibre.

SWAP & DROP

GOOD

150 *calories*

BETTER

108 *calories*

BANANA-MANGO SHAKE

SERVES 2

SHAKE
½ ripe mango

1 small ripe banana, sliced

½ cup plus 2 tbsp/150 mL 1% milk

½ cup/120 mL orange juice

2 tsp/10 mL lime juice

1 tsp/5 mL sugar

2 heaped tbsp/30 mL
vanilla frozen yogurt

GARNISH (OPTIONAL)
Sprigs of fresh lemon balm

1 Peel the skin from the mango and cut the flesh away from the stone. Chop the flesh roughly. Put into a blender with the banana.

2 Add the milk, orange juice, lime juice, sugar, and frozen yogurt and blend on maximum speed for about 30 seconds or until mixed and frothy.

3 Pour into glasses and serve immediately, decorated with sprigs of lemon balm, if you like.

PER SERVING: 5 g protein, 2 g total fat,
1 g saturated fat, 30 g carbohydrates, 1 g fibre.

STRAWBERRY-YOGURT SMOOTHIE

SERVES 4

SMOOTHIE
4 cups/1 L ripe strawberries

1 cup/250 mL plain low-fat yogurt

½ cup/125 mL fresh orange juice

1 tbsp/15 mL sugar, or to taste

GARNISH (optional)
4 small strawberries with leaves

4 thin round slices of unpeeled orange

1 Rinse and drain the strawberries and place them in a food processor or blender. Add the yogurt, orange juice, and sugar. Process on the highest speed until the mixture is a well-blended purée, about 15 seconds, stopping to scrape down the sides of the container once or twice. Taste the mixture and sweeten with a little more sugar, if you wish.

2 For a very smooth beverage, strain the mixture, using a wooden spoon to push the drink through. Discard the strawberry seeds.

3 Pour into 4 tall glasses and serve immediately. If you wish to decorate the drinks, slit the strawberries and the orange slices halfway through the centres. Attach one berry and one orange slice to the rim of each glass.

PER SERVING: 4 g protein, 2 g total fat, 1 g saturated fat, 5 mg cholesterol, 21 g carbohydrates, 4 g fibre.

MAPLE & TOASTED-WALNUT QUICK BREAD

SERVES 16

This healthy quick bread has it all: just the right amount of sweetness, a moist crumb, and the toothsome crunch of nuts throughout. The only things it doesn't have are lots of fat and cholesterol.

2 ¾ cups	self-rising flour	200 g
⅓ cup	margarine	75 mL
1 cup	maple syrup	250 mL
	1 egg, lightly beaten	
⅔ cup	evaporated fat-free milk	150 mL
1 tsp	vanilla extract	5 mL
½ cup	walnuts, toasted and chopped	125 mL

200 calories per serving

NUTS RULE!
There is some evidence to suggest that eating unsalted nuts may help relieve high blood pressure. Nuts are a good source of monounsaturated fat and are high in fibre. Walnuts, in particular, are heart healthy. They contain alpha-linolenic acid, an omega-3 fat that may lower risk for heart attack, and ellagic acid, an antioxidant compound. Store nuts in a cool, dry place or in the refrigerator for longer-lasting freshness.

1 Preheat oven to 350°F (175°C). Lightly coat a 9 x 5-inch (23 x 13-cm) loaf pan with nonstick cooking spray. Put flour into large bowl and make a well in centre.

2 Beat margarine in medium bowl with wooden spoon until creamy; blend in syrup. Beat in egg, then milk and vanilla. Pour mixture into well of flour and stir just until flour disappears. (Do not overbeat; a few lumps are okay.) Stir in walnuts.

3 Scrape batter into loaf pan. Bake until golden brown and a toothpick inserted in centre comes out with moist crumbs, about 50 minutes. If bread browns too fast, loosely cover with foil (shiny side up) during last 15 minutes of baking.

4 Cool in pan on wire rack 10 minutes. Remove from pan; serve warm or let cool completely.

PER SERVING: 4 g protein, 7 g total fat, 1 g saturated fat, 2 mg cholesterol, 31 g carbohydrates, 1 g fibre.

BERRY SALAD WITH PASSION FRUIT

Tart, sweet, and juicy, berries come in many varieties—from bright and delicate raspberries to sweet strawberries; from plump little blueberries to rich, fragrant blackberries. Thanks to importers, you can buy almost all berries in any season. If one kind is not available, you can substitute another. Fresh-squeezed passion-fruit juice adds a tart edge to the berries in this salad.

4 cups	ripe strawberries, hulled and cut in half	1 L
1 cup	fresh red raspberries	250 mL
1 cup	fresh blackberries	250 mL
½ cup	fresh blueberries	125 mL
½ cup	mixed fresh red currants and black currants removed from their stalks (optional)	125 mL
	2 passion fruits	
3 tbsp	sugar, or to taste	45 mL
1 tbsp	fresh lime or lemon juice	15 mL

89 *calories per serving*

1 In a large serving bowl, combine the strawberries, raspberries, blackberries, blueberries, red currants, and black currants.

2 Cut each passion fruit in half. Holding a strainer over the bowl of berries, spoon the passion fruit and seeds into the strainer. Press the flesh and seeds with the back of a spoon to squeeze all of the juice through the strainer onto the berries. Reserve a few of the seeds left in the strainer and discard the rest.

3 Add the sugar and lime juice to the berries. Gently toss. Sprinkle with the reserved passion-fruit seeds. Serve the salad immediately or cover and chill briefly.

PER SERVING: 1 g protein, 1 g total fat, 0 g saturated fat, 0 mg cholesterol, 22 g carbohydrates, 6 g fibre.

SWAP IT OUT!

● ● ● Omit the passion fruit. Peel, pit, and purée 2 large, ripe peaches. Sweeten with 2 tbsp (30 mL) sugar, 1 tbsp (15 mL) fresh lemon juice, and ½ tsp (5 mL) pure vanilla extract. Drizzle with 1 tbsp (15 mL) peach brandy, if you wish.

 SAVOURY TREAT

Fresh berry sundae: Scoop ½ cup (125 mL) low-fat vanilla frozen yogurt onto 6 dessert plates and spoon the berries over the top. Sprinkle with a few toasted almonds, if desired.

DROP SCONES

Drop scones, also called Scotch pancakes, are easy to make and perfect for brunch, or a simple dessert. Served with succulent berries, they are irresistible. If berry season is past, stir a diced apple into the batter and serve with a dusting of icing sugar.

SCONES		
1 cup	self-rising flour	250 mL
2 tsp	sugar	10 mL
	1 egg, beaten	
1 tbsp	margarine, melted	15 mL
½ cup	1% milk	125 mL
	Cooking spray	
GARNISH		
1 cup	blueberries	250 mL
1 cup	raspberries	250 mL
1 cup	fat-free vanilla yogurt	250 mL

152 calories per 4 scones

1 Combine the flour and sugar in a medium bowl. Make a well in the centre of the dry ingredients and add the egg, melted margarine, and a little of the milk. Gradually stir the flour into the liquids and add the remaining milk a little at a time to make a fairly thick, smooth batter.

2 Coat a large non-stick frying pan with cooking spray and heat over medium-high heat. For each scone, drop a heaping tablespoon (30 mL) of batter onto the hot surface. When bubbles form on the surface of the scones, use a spatula to turn them and then cook until the underside is golden brown, about 1 minute.

3 Remove the scones from the frying pan and keep warm under a clean cloth. Cook the rest of the batter in the same way.

4 Place the blueberries and raspberries in a bowl and lightly crush the fruit, leaving some berries whole. Serve the scones warm with the berries and vanilla yogurt.

PER SERVING: 5 g protein, 2 g total fat, 1 g saturated fat, 37 mg cholesterol, 27 g carbohydrates, 3 g fibre.

SWAP the Flavour

PARMESAN & HERB drop scones: Instead of sugar add 1 tbsp (15 mL) snipped chives, 1 tbsp (15 mL) chopped fresh oregano, and 2 tbsp (30 mL) freshly grated Parmesan cheese to the flour. Serve the drop scones topped with low-fat plain yogurt or cottage cheese and halved cherry tomatoes.

Swap & Drop brunch

As they walk in the door— Offer guests a flute of champagne or mimosa. Champagne, you'll be delighted to hear, is a naturally diet-friendly drink at just 110 calories for a 5-ounce (150 mL) glass.

kids

Fill kids' glasses (if they're old enough, let them enjoy the flutes, too!) with fruit sparklers dressed up with a swizzle stick stacked with cubes and slices of fresh fruit. Add a happy fizz by mixing fruit juice with an equal amount of no-cal soda water.

party! planner

When you're THE HOST

▶ The perennial problem with brunch is the tendency of recipes to require last-minute—or continuous—personal attention. That's just fine for a lazy family-only Sunday, when flipping crêpes, pancakes, or waffles straight from the hot grill is part of the fun, but you want a different, make-ahead approach for company. This menu fits the bill:

When you're THE GUEST

▶ Alternate any alcoholic drink with a glass of water, fizzy or not.

▶ Ask for tea or coffee to which you add your own milk and sugar; stay away from liqueur-added brews or those with whipped cream toppers. An Irish coffee will pack on 100 calories or more, a Spanish close to 300 or more. Black coffee or clear tea? A big, fat zero! And they can offer health benefits to boot.

▶ Load your plate, or ask your host to load it, with double the fruit or veg and half the breads or proteins.

▶ Choose bacon over sausage, selecting the crispier pieces.

▶ Eat slowly; savour every bite and start a few conversations!

Menu

Tomato & Romano Cheese Bake (page 106)
• *This recipe is ideal for guests. The cheery red of cherry tomatoes is the epitome of eye candy. Served in individual ovenproof dishes, the presentation is spectacular.*

Young greens
• *Add a simple side salad of young greens dressed with one of our many flavourful vinaigrettes (pages 64-67).*

Fresh multi-grain bread & whipped butter

Coffee & dessert >>>

COFFEE & DESSERT

• **Dessert is a luscious and unexpected finale to any brunch**, but don't agonize over a complicated recipe. This is the time to give fresh fruit the upper hand. The trick is to **find a fun way to serve it up**; for any party, a little effort in presentation goes a long way. • **In summer**, fill your fanciest shot glasses with plump berries and serve on a dessert plate with a mini meringue or butter cookie on the side. • **In winter**, simmer frozen or fresh berries with a sprinkling of sugar until they burst their skins, and drizzle on a slender slice of angel food cake. • End the meal by **indulging in a flavoured coffee**, but hold off on the cream.

LEEK & PROSCIUTTO PIZZA MUFFINS

SERVES 4

Leeks, basil, and prosciutto combine with mozzarella to make a sophisticated pizza-style topping for whole-wheat muffins. Serve with a simple salad of arugula and grated carrot tossed with extra virgin olive oil and lemon juice.

SWAP
the Flavour

Use 2 ounces (60 g) lean **COOKED HAM**, cut into fine strips, instead of the prosciutto, and extra small arugula leaves instead of the basil.

1 tbsp	extra virgin olive oil	15 mL
	2 leeks, thinly sliced	
	Pepper to taste	
	4 whole-wheat English muffins, halved	
	Handful of shredded fresh basil leaves	
	4 slices prosciutto, trimmed of visible fat and halved crosswise	
3 ounces	mozzarella cheese, cut into thin strips	90 g
	GARNISH	
¼ cup	coarsely chopped arugula	60 mL

269 calories per serving

1 Heat the oil in a saucepan, add the leeks and cook over medium-high heat, stirring frequently, for about 5 minutes or until the leeks are tender and the juices have evaporated. Season with pepper.

2 Preheat the broiler. Place the muffins, cut-side down, on the broiler rack. Toast the bases, then turn the muffins over. Divide the leeks equally among the muffins. Top with the basil, then place a piece of prosciutto on each muffin half. Gently pinch the prosciutto up into loose folds. Scatter the strips of mozzarella cheese over the top.

3 Cook the muffin pizzas under the broiler until the mozzarella cheese has melted and is bubbling. The prosciutto and cheese should be lightly browned in places. Sprinkle with the chopped arugula and serve.

PER SERVING: 17 g protein, 12 g total fat, 5 g saturated fat, 22 mg cholesterol, 23 g carbohydrates, 4 g fibre.

CREAM CHEESE, BANANA & COCONUT PAIN PERDU SERVES 4

Pain perdu, the French name for French toast, is a great brunch treat or a surprising dinner party dessert. Caramelizing the bananas gives a texture and flavour variation that elevates this everyday fruit.

Research shows that yogurt and bananas, consumed together after exercise, speed muscle recovery. Combining carbs (banana) and protein (yogurt) increases insulin levels, which allows muscles to soak up repair nutrients like amino acids and glucose, says Monique Ryan, a sports dietitian and author of *Sports Nutrition for Endurance Athletes.*

¼ cup	coconut, shredded, unsweetened	60 mL
	1 egg	
1 tbsp	skim milk	15 mL
1 tbsp	rum	15 mL
2 tsp	unsalted butter	10 mL
	8 slices baguette, each 1-inch (2.5-cm) thick	
3 tbsp	light cream cheese	45 mL
1	banana, cut diagonally into 8 slices 1-inch (2.5-cm) thick	
4 tsp	maple syrup	20 mL

378 calories per serving

1 Preheat oven to 350°F (175°C). Toast shredded coconut on a baking sheet for a few minutes until lightly brown. Remove from baking sheet and set aside.

2 Beat egg, milk, and rum together.

3 Melt 1 tsp (5 mL) butter in a medium sauté pan on medium heat. Dip each slice of bread in egg mixture and place in pan. Cook on both sides until golden brown. Remove from pan.

4 Spread cream cheese thinly on one side of each slice. Set aside. Add remaining butter to pan. Place banana slices in pan and cook, turning once, until lightly brown and caramelized on both sides.

5 Place a cooked banana piece on top of each bread slice. To serve, set two pieces on each plate. Top with toasted coconut and a drizzle of maple syrup.

PER SERVING: 11 g protein, 14 g total fat, 11 g saturated fat, 11 mg cholesterol., 53 g carbohydrates, 5 g fibre.

PERFECT PARFAIT
Layer banana slices with mango, pineapple and papaya. Top with granola

SWAP & DROP
FAST FOOD

SWAP THIS | FOR THAT

BOOSTER JUICE

Matcha Monsoon (matcha green tea powder, vanilla soy milk, vanilla frozen yogurt)

500 calories

8 g fat

330 mg sodium

1 g fibre

Mango Hurricane (mango, peaches, passion fruit, guava, strawberries, yogurt)

290 calories

0.3 g fat

50 mg sodium

3 g fibre

MMMUFFINS

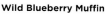

Wild Blueberry Muffin

500 calories

30 g fat (2.5 g saturated)

24 g sugars

370 mg sodium

Blueberry Scone

270 calories

8 g fat (2 g saturated)

7 g sugars

720 mg sodium

A&W

Deluxe Bacon & Eggs (3 eggs, 5 strips of bacon, 2 slices of white toast, margarine)

750 calories

48 g fat (14 g saturated)

1,180 mg sodium

Bacon N' Egger (egg, processed cheddar cheese, bacon, sesame seed bun, margarine)

430 calories

27 g fat (8 g saturated)

900 mg sodium

TIM HORTONS

Mocha latte, medium (espresso, cocoa, milk, whip topping with a chocolate drizzle)

230 calories

7 g fat (6 g saturated)

200 mg sodium

Latte, medium
(espresso, milk)

100 calories

0.3 g fat (0.2 g saturated)

160 mg sodium

2

LIGHT FARE

2 Light Fare Healthy small meals are as important as having a good variety of snacks in your arsenal

We've called this chapter light fare, knowing that sometimes you'll want to swap supper for lunch, and vice versa. Just control your overall daily calorie count by keeping tab of your daily total, whether it's to lose a few pounds or to keep your weight steady.

These recipes include at least one, and many contain two, servings of vegetables. No other food fills you up on fewer calories with more nutrients. One serving is half a cup, or what you can hold in your cupped hand. If the lunch you crave is light on veggies, add a small side salad, some celery sticks, one large carrot or a broccoli floret, three tomato slices... whatever suits your taste.

One last bit of advice: don't skip lunch! After reviewing research on eating habits, researchers at the University of Missouri concluded in 2011 that there was no sizable difference in hunger pangs or feelings of fullness for those who eat three meals a day or several smaller meals throughout the day. Eating just two meals a day, however, was linked to increased appetite, and a reduced feeling of fullness; a good recipe for overeating!

Plan for a healthy lunch
Serve up delicious swaps for lighter midday meals

Don't let lunch and your busy day blindside you–always plan ahead. And remember, adjusting recipes, cooking techniques, and even presentation can combine for big calorie savings.

Your favourite meals, the ones you whip up in a hurry, don't have to be ditched on the **Swap & Drop Diet**. Ingredients can be lightened, their preparation revised, and, easiest of all, there are calorie-wise ways to serve them up. Here are ideas to get you started:

Intelligent ingredients

Veggie versions. Cut back on meat and add extra vegetables. Skimp on lunch meat and pump up the volume with sliced tomato or cucumber, some alfalfa sprouts, or extra lettuce. Ditto for fruit: mound a generous portion of berries on a single pancake. An added bonus: fibre and vitamins rise as calories plummet.

Nice spread. When making sandwiches, swap mayo for mashed avocado that, at 24 calories a tablespoon and 2 grams of fat, is much lighter than even light mayo, which comes in at 50 calories and 5 grams of fat.

Yummy yogurt. When a recipe calls for sour cream or mayonnaise, try swapping in plain, fat-free yogurt for ¾ of the amount. Its tangy zip delivers on flavour but contains just 100 calories per cup (250 mL), while just one tablespoon of mayonnaise is 90 calories with 10 grams of fat. Sour cream is 60 calories and 5 grams of fat (light versions are about 20 calories and 2.5 grams of fat).

Think salsa. Dress up meats, fish, and seafood with fresh salsas made with fruit and veggies. They add a hefty hit of taste without a high calorie count.

Pick up a lemon. Swap out one can of sweet soda and, instead, sip iced water with a squeeze of lemon or lime, or a couple of crushed mint leaves, to save 140 calories. Do this daily to save a whopping 51,100 calories, or 14.6 pounds, in a year.

Go naked. Keep away from fatty cheese sauce–try cauliflower and broccoli steamed, with a dash of balsamic vinegar and a generous grind of pepper, or the lightest touch of salt.

Great grate. Swap in grated carrots or oatmeal for some of the meat in meatloaf and meatballs. Or use ground chicken or turkey instead of lean ground beef in your spaghetti sauce and chili.

A flaky idea. Don't dip your fillets in egg and coat with bread crumbs; dip in water and coat with crushed cornflakes.

Best cooking methods

Broil, grill, poach, bake, roast, sauté, steam, or microwave your food. Baste with fat-free vegetable broth, juice, or wine. Buy non-stick cookware and use non-stick spray. Sauté with beer, wine, or low-salt vegetable broth–onions sauté beautifully in a little water if you cover the pot and reduce heat after bringing to a boil.

Serve it up right

Keep condiments off the table. Salt, sugar, and fat give traditional condiments their kick. Instead, perk up the flavour of your meals with a dash of hot sauce, a sprinkling of herbs, or hit of spices.

Smaller dishes really do work; the trend towards large plates has us piling on the food to fill them. Take a look at your grandmother's everyday china. Chances are they're about 9 inches (23 cm) across. Take a look at yours. They're probably the current norm of about 11 inches (28 cm). That's a 50% increase in surface area; you can fit generous seconds in your first portion!

Start with smaller portions, and chew slowly. Take time to allow your body to feel full.

Delay having seconds until at least 20 minutes after you started to eat, the time it takes for your stomach to alert your brain that it's had enough.

Are you !#*@%?& kidding me?

University of California researchers found that volunteers thought they were drinking regular tomato juice when it was really a low-sodium variety spiked with a squirt of lemon. Their conclusion? The zesty lemon flavour fools the taste buds into thinking it's salt. So don't tip the shaker, squeeze a wedge instead!

**SWAP UP
FIBRE**
Increase the fibre content
and make a more sub-
stantial meal by adding
1 can (14 ounces/398 mL)
red kidney or cannellini
beans, drained and rinsed,
with the pasta.

There's nothing like a tasty salad to satisfy the senses. This dish can easily grab star status: brightly coloured ingredients draw the eye and a rich mix of flavours tempt the tongue. Bonus: a salad's silky, crunchy textures can help you resist other silky, crunchy choices (full-cream soups, deep fried anything) that are far less good for you.

PIQUANT PASTA & TUNA SALAD

SERVES 4

This salad, with its sweet-and-sour dressing, is a great twist on tuna casserole. Serve it cool or while still warm, accompanied by wedges of juicy cantaloupe.

435 calories per serving

8 ounces	pasta twists or spirals	250 g
2 tbsp	olive oil	30 mL
	1 onion, chopped	
	1 garlic clove, chopped	
	2 zucchini, thinly sliced	
2 tsp	sugar	10 mL
2 tbsp	red or green pesto	30 mL
1 tbsp	white or red wine vinegar	15 mL
1 tbsp	capers	15 mL
	6 tomatoes, halved and cut into thin wedges	
1 6-ounce can	water-packed solid white tuna, drained and roughly flaked	1 184-g can
	6 black olives, pitted and halved	
	GARNISH	
	Fresh flat-leaf parsley	

1 Cook the pasta in boiling water for 10 to 12 minutes, or according to package instructions, until al dente. Drain well, rinse with cold water, and drain again.

2 While the pasta is cooking, heat 1 tbsp (15 mL) of the oil in a saucepan. Add the onion and garlic, and sauté for 3 minutes, stirring often. Add the remaining oil and the zucchini and cook, stirring occasionally, for 3 minutes.

3 Add the sugar, pesto, vinegar, and capers to the onion and zucchini. Heat for a few seconds, stirring until the ingredients have combined to form a dressing. Stir in the tomatoes, then transfer the mixture to a large mixing bowl and set aside to cool.

4 Add the drained pasta to the bowl, then gently mix in the tuna and olives. Divide among 4 plates or transfer to a large serving bowl. Serve garnished with flat-leaf parsley leaves, if desired.

PER SERVING: 22 g protein, 12 g total fat, 1 g saturated fat, 13 mg cholesterol, 62 g carbohydrates, 6 g fibre.

MEDITERRANEAN SALAD WITH EDAMAME

Torn leaves of fragrant herbs and delicate, protein-rich edamame beans distinguish this variation of a classic Greek salad. Edamame are immature soybeans found in natural foods stores or in your supermarket freezer or natural foods sections.

220 calories per serving

1 cup	frozen shelled edamame beans	250 mL
1/3 cup	extra-virgin olive oil	75 mL
3 tbsp	lemon juice	45 mL
	2 garlic cloves, minced	
1/4 tsp	sugar	1 mL
2 cups	shredded romaine lettuce (1/2 small head)	500 mL
2 cups	cherry tomatoes, halved, or 2 medium tomatoes, cut into 1-inch (2.5-cm) wedges	500 mL
1 cup	sliced English cucumber	250 mL
2/3 cup	chopped green onions	150 mL
1/2 cup	pitted kalamata olives, halved	125 mL
1/2 cup	fresh mint leaves, washed, dried, and torn into 1/2-inch (1-cm) pieces	125 mL
1/2 cup	fresh flat-leaf parsley, washed, dried, and torn into 1/2-inch (1-cm) pieces	125 mL
1 cup	crumbled feta cheese	250 mL
	Salt and pepper, to taste	

1 Bring a large saucepan of lightly salted water to a boil. Add the edamame beans and cook, covered, over medium heat until tender, 3 to 4 minutes. Drain and rinse with cold running water.

2 Combine the oil, lemon juice, garlic, salt, sugar, and pepper in a screw-top jar with a tight-fitting lid. Shake to blend.

3 Combine the lettuce, tomatoes, cucumber, green onions, olives, mint, parsley, and cooked edamame beans in a large bowl. Just before serving, drizzle the lemon dressing over salad and toss to coat well. Sprinkle each serving with feta.

PER SERVING: 7 g protein, 17 g total fat, 5 g saturated fat, 15 mg cholesterol, 10 g carbohydrates, 3 g fibre.

:) DYNAMIC DUO

Scientists in Korea have discovered that genistein (found in edamame, tofu, and other soy foods), when mixed with capsaicin (a compound found in hot peppers) helps tame inflammation. Chronic inflammation is a risk factor for heart disease and cancer. Put that in your stir-fry!

SPICY RICE SALAD WITH PINEAPPLE

SERVES 4

Far East flavours blend beautifully for a summery salad any time of year.

1 cup	basmati rice	250 mL
¼ tsp	salt	2 mL
1 cup	drained canned pineapple slices or pieces in natural juice	250 mL
	4 stalks celery	
3 cups	small mushrooms, chopped	750 mL
	2 green onions, sliced	
	4 to 6 large Chinese (napa) cabbage leaves	
CURRY VINAIGRETTE		
⅓ cup	crème fraîche or light sour cream	80 mL
3 tbsp	milk	45 mL
2 tbsp	raspberry vinegar	30 mL
1 tbsp	sunflower oil	15 mL
¼ tsp	ground ginger	1 mL
1 tsp	mild curry powder	5 mL
¼ to ½ tsp	sambal oelek (Chinese chili paste)	1 to 2 mL

370 calories per serving

COOK'S TIP

Basmati is an aromatic rice native to Pakistan and India. It is good for steaming or boiling. When cooked, the grains swell lengthwise only, and stay separate and dry.

1 Place rice in a saucepan with 1 ¾ cups (400 mL) water and ½ tsp salt. Bring to a boil, uncovered. Cover pan and cook rice over low heat 15 to 20 minutes or until all liquid is absorbed. Rice should be light and fluffy with steam holes on the surface. Turn off heat, let stand, covered, another 5 minutes. Remove from heat, uncover pan and let rice cool. Loosen grains with a fork.

2 Chop pineapple slices into small pieces. Slice celery into thin strips. Reserve feathery leaves. Combine rice, pineapple, celery, and mushrooms in a large bowl. Add green onions, reserving a few for garnish.

3 To make dressing, whisk crème fraîche, milk, vinegar, oil, ginger, curry, and ¼ tsp sambal oelek in a bowl until creamy. Add remaining ¼ tsp (1 mL) sambal oelek to taste.

4 Cut Chinese cabbage leaves into strips. Divide among individual serving plates and top with rice salad. Garnish with celery leaves and reserved green onion rings.

PER SERVING: 8 g protein, 16 g total fat, 9 g saturated fat, 33 mg cholesterol, 47 g carbohydrate, 6 g fibre.

EGG & RADISH SALAD

Both of the salad greens used in this recipe have a slightly bitter taste that is complemented by peppery heat of the radishes.

229 calories per serving

	2 medium eggs, hard–boiled	
	8 large frisée (curly endive) lettuce leaves	
	2 medium heads endive or chicory	
	2 green onions	
	16 medium red radishes	
	CREAM CHEESE DRESSING	
4 ounces	low-fat cream cheese, plain or herbed	100 g
3 tbsp	yogurt	45 mL
2 tbsp	herb vinegar	30 mL
2 tbsp	canola oil	30 mL
2 tbsp	finely chopped fresh herbs, such as a mix of parsley, chives, dill, chervil, sorrel	30 mL
	Salt and freshly ground black pepper, to taste	

1 Slice eggs into thin rounds. Divide frisée among serving plates. Place endive or chicory leaves on top, open sides upwards.

2 Finely chop white part of green onions; slice green part into thin rounds and set aside. Finely dice radishes. Mix with white part of green onions.

3 Make dressing: combine cream cheese, yogurt, vinegar, and oil. Add herbs, reserving a little for garnish. Season with salt and pepper.

4 Sprinkle radish/green onion mixture evenly over the lettuces. Top with dressing. Add egg slices. Sprinkle with remaining herbs and green parts of green onions.

PER SERVING: 7 g protein, 21 g total fat, 7 g saturated fat, 134 mg cholesterol, 2 g carbohydrates, 1 g fibre.

SHOPPING

What's in a designer egg?

Eggs vary little in nutrition from one brand to the next, with two exceptions. One is eggs fortified with heart-smart omega-3s, usually attained by adding flax-seed to the chickens' feed. Each egg typically provides 150 to 200 mg of omega-3s—a small fraction of the amount you'd get from eating fish. The other exception is reduced-cholesterol eggs, which contain 25% less than regular ones. These are usually produced by feeding chicken a vegetarian diet high in canola oil.

COLOUR FIESTA!
Researchers have concluded that colour affects how people expect food will taste before it ever touches their lips. Inviting colours like these give the brain a treat before the taste buds.

EASTERN SALAD

Based on fattoush—the colourful, crunchy salad served throughout the Middle East—this version adds tuna for extra flavour and protein. Make sure you grill the pita bread until it is really crisp to prevent it from going soggy when mixed with the other ingredients, and serve the salad as soon as possible after making it.

	4 small whole-wheat pita breads	
1 ½ tbsp	olive oil	20 mL
	Juice of 1 lemon	
	6 green onions, sliced	
¾ pound	ripe tomatoes, chopped	375 g
	1 small cucumber, diced	
1 6-ounce	can tuna, drained and flaked	1 170-g
2 tbsp	coarsely chopped fresh flat-leaf parsley	30 mL
1 tbsp	coarsely chopped fresh cilantro	15 mL
1 tbsp	coarsely chopped fresh mint	15 mL
	Salt and pepper, to taste	

270 calories per serving

1 Preheat the broiler. Place the pita breads on a baking sheet and warm under the broiler, 6 inches (15 cm) from the heat source, for a few seconds or until puffy, then carefully split them open through the middle and open out each one like a book. Return to the broiler and toast on each side or until lightly browned and crisp, about 2 to 3 minutes. Roughly tear the pita into bite-size pieces and set aside.

2 Whisk together the olive oil and lemon juice in a large serving bowl, and season lightly with salt and pepper. Add the green onions, tomatoes, cucumber, and tuna, and toss gently to coat with the oil and lemon juice.

3 Add the parsley, cilantro, mint, and torn pita pieces to the serving bowl and toss quickly to mix. Serve at once.

PER SERVING: 18 g protein, 7 g total fat, 1 g saturated fat, 13 mg cholesterol, 38 g carbohydrates, 4 g fibre.

1 MORE IDEA

● ● ● **Mediterranean-Style Vegetable Salad**

Whisk together 1 tsp (5 mL) Dijon mustard, 1 tsp (5 mL) finely grated lemon zest, 1 crushed garlic clove, 2 tsp (10 mL) red wine vinegar, 1 ½ tsp (7 mL olive oil), 1 tsp (5 mL) chopped fresh oregano, and salt and pepper to taste in a large serving bowl. Quarter a ½ pound (250 g) of baby plum tomatoes and add to the bowl. Add 2 medium zucchini, 1 small bulb of fennel, and 1 red onion, all coarsely chopped. Toss to coat the vegetables with the dressing.

GARDEN PASTA SALAD

Pasta salads are perfect for potlucks, picnics, and backyard barbecues. This version has been upgraded with whole wheat pasta and a generous quantity of colourful vegetables. Reduced-fat mayonnaise, blended with low-fat yogurt, makes a creamy dressing that has a fraction of the saturated fat and calories of typical mayonnaise dressings. It keeps, covered, in the refrigerator for up to 1 day.

2 cups	uncooked whole wheat rotini or fusilli pasta	500 mL
⅓ cup	reduced-fat mayonnaise	75 mL
⅓ cup	low-fat plain yogurt	75 mL
2 tbsp	extra-virgin olive oil	30 mL
1 tbsp	red-wine vinegar or lemon juice	15 mL
	1 garlic clove, minced	
	Salt and pepper, to taste	
1 cup	cherry or grape tomatoes, halved	250 mL
1 cup	diced yellow or red pepper (1 small)	250 mL
1 cup	grated carrots (2-4 medium)	250 mL
½ cup	chopped green onions (4 medium)	125 mL
½ cup	chopped pitted kalamata olives	125 mL
⅓ cup	slivered fresh basil	75 mL

205 *calories per serving*

GREAT ADD-ON

● ● ● If you'd like to make this salad more substantial, toss in canned tuna (packed in water, not oil, of course!), cooked chicken, or chickpeas.

1 Bring a large pot of lightly salted water to a boil. Cook pasta, stirring often, until al dente, 8 to 10 minutes, or according to package directions. Drain and refresh under cold running water.

2 Whisk mayonnaise, yogurt, oil, vinegar, garlic, salt, and pepper in a large bowl until smooth. Add the pasta and toss to coat. Add the tomatoes, pepper, carrots, green onions, olives, and basil. Toss to coat well.

PER SERVING: 6 g protein, 9 g total fat, 2 g saturated fat, 1 mg cholesterol, 29 g carbohydrates, 4 g fibre.

ASIAN BEAN SPROUT SALAD

SERVES 4

Mung bean sprouts and peanuts add crunch to this salad. Mung beans have a hint of sweetness. In Chinese medicine, they are considered a yin, or cooling, food.

272 calories per serving

5 ounces	mung bean sprouts	150 g
	2 green onions, sliced into rounds	
	4 medium celery stalks, thinly sliced	
	1 medium mango or 2 small nectarines	
	½ small fresh pineapple (about 1 pound/500 g)	
	4 to 6 large Chinese (napa) cabbage leaves	
4 tbsp	coarsely chopped roasted peanuts	60 mL
	SPICY FRUIT DRESSING	
2 tbsp	raspberry vinegar	30 mL
3 tbsp	olive oil	45 mL
4 tbsp	orange juice	60 mL
¼ tsp-½ tsp	sambal oelek (Chinese chili paste)	1-2 mL
½ tsp-1 tsp	ground ginger	2-5 mL
¼ tsp-½ tsp	finely grated lemon peel	1-2 mL

1 Combine sprouts, green onions and celery in a large bowl. Peel mango and slice flesh thinly. Peel pineapple and cut into small chunks. Add to bowl.

2 To make spicy fruit dressing, whisk all the ingredients in a small bowl until combined. Stir into salad.

3 Cut Chinese cabbage leaves into wide strips. Distribute among serving plates. Add bean sprout salad and sprinkle with peanuts.

PER SERVING: 6 g protein, 19 g total fat, 3 g saturated fat, 0 mg cholesterol, 19 g carbohydrates, 6 g fibre.

INGREDIENT INTEL

A **sambal** is a fresh or cooked relish. Sambal oelek is a spicy chili paste often used in conjunction with other sambal ingredients. It is made from ground chili peppers, salt, and vinegar or tamarind. Tamarind is a very acidic fruit that gives sambals a particularly sharp taste. In a traditional oelek, the chili peppers are not seeded, adding extra heat.

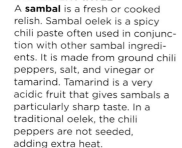

BEAN SALAD WITH PAPRIKA VINAIGRETTE

Vinaigrettes offer a range of tastes and can be endlessly varied by using flavoured vinegars and different herbs and spices. More vinaigrettes are on pages 64 to 67.

280 calories per serving

1 pound	broad (fava) beans (frozen or shelled fresh)	500 g
	1 small cucumber	
	2 shallots, finely diced	
	3 Italian (plum) tomatoes, sliced	
	1 small red and 1 yellow pepper, seeded and diced	
½ cup	finely chopped fresh flat-leaf parsley	125 mL
	PAPRIKA VINAIGRETTE	
4 tbsp	olive oil	60 mL
2 tbsp	balsamic vinegar	30 mL
1 tbsp	lemon juice	15 mL
1 tbsp	ground cumin	15 mL
½ tsp	ground sweet paprika	2 mL
	Pinch of cayenne pepper	
	Pinch of freshly ground black pepper	

1 Place beans in a saucepan. Cover with water; bring to a boil. Cook 15 minutes or unti crisp-tender. Drain and let cool:

2 Cut cucumber in half lengthwise and remove seeds. Slice thinly, add beans, shallots, and tomatoes.

3 Whisk vinaigrette ingredients together until combined; stir in peppers.

4 Arrange on individual plates. Drizzle dressing on salad; sprinkle with parsley.

PER SERVING: 12 g protein, 19 g total fat, 3 g saturated fat, 0 mg cholesterol, 14 g carbohydrates, 8 g fibre.

SWAP IT OUT!

● ● ● **Bean Salad with Creamy Dressing**

Cook broad (fava) beans as described in main recipe and allow to cool. Peel and finely dice 2 shallots and place in a bowl with the broad beans. To make dressing, whisk 2 tbsp (30 mL) white wine vinegar, 1 tbsp (15 mL) olive oil, 3 tbsp (45 mL) whipping cream, 2 tbsp (30 mL) crème fraîche or light sour cream, salt, and freshly ground black pepper to taste. Stir dressing into salad. Cover and refrigerate 30 minutes. Serve with whole-grain bread.

ROOT VEGETABLE SALAD & SPICY VINAIGRETTE SERVES 4

Select small beets with their greens still attached; they have the most flavour.

1 pound	beets	500 g
1 pound	waxy potatoes	500 g
	3 medium tomatoes	
	2 green onions, finely chopped	
	2 cloves garlic, finely chopped	
¼ cup	finely chopped fresh flat-leaf parsley	60 mL
	3 sprigs cilantro leaves, finely chopped	
⅔ cup	black olives, for garnish	160 mL
	SPICY VINAIGRETTE	
5 tbsp	white wine vinegar	75 mL
6 tbsp	olive oil	90 mL
	Salt and pepper, to taste	
	Pinch of cayenne pepper	

381 calories per serving

1 Place beets in a large saucepan, cover with water, and bring to a boil. Simmer 1 ½ hours, or until a fork is easily inserted. Drain, reserving 4 tbsp liquid. Rinse with cold water; let cool.

2 Cook potatoes in boiling water 20 to 30 minutes, or until just cooked. Drain, rinse with cold water; let cool. Peel beets and potatoes, halve, and slice thinly. Place in separate bowls.

3 Plunge tomatoes into boiling water for 1 minute. Transfer to bowl of iced water. Peel tomatoes, cut in halves, remove seeds, and dice flesh. Combine tomatoes and green onions with beets. Add garlic, parsley, cilantro, and reserved cooking water.

4 Make vinaigrette: whisk vinegar, oil, salt, pepper, and cayenne pepper until combined. Stir two-thirds vinaigrette into beet mixture and remainder into potatoes. Cover and refrigerate 30 minutes.

5 Just before serving, add salt, pepper, and vinegar to taste. Spoon beet salad onto a platter and arrange potato salad around it. Garnish with olives.

PER SERVING: 5 g protein, 28 g total fat, 4 g saturated fat, 0 mg cholesterol, 27 g carbohydrates, 6 g fibre.

SHOPPING

How to pick the best beets

Select small to medium-sized beets with firm, smooth skin and a deep colour. Store unwashed for up to 3 weeks in the fridge; wrap them in a plastic bag with as much air squeezed out as possible.

GADO GADO

SERVES 6

Gado means "mixed". This traditional Indonesian specialty is a combination of raw and lightly cooked vegetables served with spicy peanut sauce. Serve warm or at room temperature.

382 calories per serving

A bite of history

🢒 Gado gado ingredients vary from one region to another. Additions can include spinach, snow peas, or cauliflower. Firm veggies should be served either raw, blanched, or steamed; if cooked, they should remain crunchy.

	1 small head iceberg lettuce, leaves separated	
	2 large potatoes, boiled and sliced	
1 cup	green beans, sliced, blanched	200 g
¾ cup	bean sprouts, blanched	80 g
1 ½ cups	shredded Chinese (napa) cabbage, blanched	375 mL
	2 medium tomatoes, cut into wedges	
	1 medium red onion, sliced	
	3 spring onions, cut in short lengths	
	1 Lebanese (or 1 small) cucumber, thinly sliced	
	2 fresh red chili peppers, seeded and thinly sliced	
	4 medium hard-boiled eggs, sliced	
3 ounces	fried firm tofu, cut into cubes	125 g
	PEANUT SAUCE	
½ cup	vegetable oil	90 g
1 ¼ cups	raw unsalted peanuts	310 mL
	2 cloves garlic, chopped	
	4 green onions, chopped	
	salt	
½ tsp	chili powder	2 mL
1 tsp	soft brown sugar	5 mL
1 tbsp	dark, sodium-reduced soy sauce	15 mL
2 cups	water	500 ml
	Juice of 1 lemon	

1 Arrange lettuce leaves on a large plate. Add all the remaining salad ingredients in small groups (for people to help themselves). Serve peanut sauce separately.

2 To make peanut sauce, heat oil in a wok or frying pan over high heat. Stir-fry peanuts until light golden brown, about 4 minutes. Remove with a slotted spoon and place on paper towel to cool. Pound or process peanuts until finely ground. Discard oil from pan, reserving 1 tbsp (15 mL).

3 Crush garlic and green onions in a mortar and pestle with a little salt. Fry in reserved oil, about 1 minute. Add chili powder, sugar, soy sauce, and water. Bring to a boil; add ground peanuts. Simmer, stirring occasionally, until sauce is thick, about 10 minutes. Add lemon juice and more salt, if needed. Cool. (Sauce can be made ahead and stored in a jar in the refrigerator for up to 1 week.)

PER SERVING: 18 g protein, 27 g total fat, 4 g saturated fat, 143 mg cholesterol, 17 g carbohydrates, 9 g fibre.

WATERMELON & FETA SALAD

In this salad, the salty tang of creamy feta cheese contrasts with chunks of sweet watermelon and juicy golden nectarines. A mix of arugula, endive, and leaf lettuce adds a slightly peppery taste, while the toasted pumpkin seeds give it a nice crunch. The dressing is light and zesty, complementing the flavours of the salad perfectly. Serve with whole-wheat bread for a light lunch or supper.

198 calories per serving

	1 small watermelon (about 1 pound/500 g)	
	2 large nectarines or peaches	
6 cups	mixed salad greens, including arugula, endive, and leaf lettuce	1.5 L
1 cup	crumbled feta cheese	250 mL
2 tbsp	toasted pumpkin seeds or sunflower seeds	30 mL
	LEMON DRESSING	
3 tbsp	olive oil	45 mL
2 tbsp	fresh lemon juice	30 mL
¼ tsp	salt	1 mL
¼ tsp	freshly ground black pepper	1 mL

1 First, make the dressing. Place the oil, lemon juice, salt, and pepper into a 2-cup (500-mL) jar or container with a tight-fitting lid. Cover and shake until well blended.

2 Using a serrated knife, cut the watermelon into bite-sized chunks, discarding the rind and all of the seeds. Place in a large salad bowl.

3 Cut the nectarines in half (do not peel) and pit them. Place them on a cutting board, cut side down, and slice thinly lengthwise; add to the watermelon chunks. Tear the salad greens into bite-sized pieces and add to the fruit. Toss gently to mix.

4 Crumble the feta cheese over the salad. Sprinkle the seeds over the top and drizzle with the lemon dressing; serve.

PER SERVING: 6 g protein, 15 g total fat, 5 g saturated fat, 22 mg cholesterol, 13 g carbohydrates, 2 g fibre.

SWAP IT OUT!

● ● ● **Pear & Gorgonzola Salad**

Instead of watermelon and nectarines, use 1 pound (500 g) ripe, cored, thinly sliced red Bartlett or Comice pears and 3 cups (750 mL) sliced ripe strawberries. Use 1 cup (250 mL) creamy Gorgonzola cheese instead of the feta. Include radicchio in the mix of salad leaves. Try using toasted walnuts in place of the toasted pumpkin or sunflower seeds.

LISTEN UP, LADIES!
A recent study showed that 25% of Canadian women don't get enough vitamin C; the best food sources are fresh fruit, also brassica veggies (like broccoli).

TARRAGON CHICKEN SALAD

Tahini, a ground sesame paste available from most large supermarkets, adds a nutty taste and creaminess to the dressing for this colourful and nutritious chicken salad. The chicken is served on a bed of crisp spinach leaves and topped with crunchy toasted almonds for a snappy presentation.

1 pound	boneless, skinless chicken breasts	500 g
1 ½ cups	reduced-sodium chicken or vegetable broth	375 mL
	1 small bunch fresh tarragon	
	1 small lemon	
	3 black peppercorns	
2 tbsp	sesame tahini	30 mL
	1 head chicory or other head lettuce	
2 cups	baby spinach leaves	500 mL
	2 oranges	
¼ cup	toasted sliced almonds	60 mL
	Pepper	

273 calories per serving

INGREDIENT INTEL

Tahini contains 16 grams of fat per 2 tbsp (30 mL), but only a little of the potent ingredient is needed to give a unique, flavourful dressing.

Chicory was used by the ancient Egyptians, Greeks, and Romans, both for cooking and its medicinal properties. It was believed to stimulate the digestive juices and strengthen the liver.

1 Place the chicken breasts in a shallow pan, in one layer, and pour in the broth. Remove the tarragon leaves from the stalks and set aside. Lightly crush the tarragon stalks with a rolling pin to release all their oils, then add to the pan. Using a vegetable peeler, remove a small strip of zest from the lemon and add this to the pan together with the peppercorns.

2 Set the pan over medium heat and bring the broth to a boil. Turn down the heat so the broth just simmers gently and cover the pan. Cook until the chicken is cooked all the way through, about 15 minutes.

3 Remove the chicken breasts, using a slotted spoon, and let cool on a plate. Strain the broth into a bowl and discard the tarragon stalks, lemon zest, and peppercorns. Set the broth aside. When the chicken has cooled, cut it into thick strips.

4 Add the tahini to a mixing bowl and gradually whisk in 4 tbsp (60 mL) of the reserved broth to make a smooth, creamy dressing. If the dressing is a bit thick, whisk in another 1 to 2 tbsp (15 to 30 mL) of the broth. Squeeze the juice from the lemon and stir it into the dressing. Chop enough of the tarragon leaves to make 1 tbsp (15 mL), and add to the dressing with pepper to taste.

5 Cut the chicory or other lettuce diagonally into slices about 1 inch (2.5 cm) wide. Arrange the chicory and spinach in a large salad bowl.

6 Peel the oranges, then divide into segments. Scatter the segments over the salad leaves, followed by the toasted almonds. Place the chicken strips on top, and spoon over the tahini tarragon dressing. Serve at once.

PER SERVING: 30 g protein, 11 g total fat, 1 g saturated fat, 67 mg cholesterol, 14 g carbohydrates, 5 g fibre.

JAMAICAN CHICKEN SALAD

SERVES 4

Assemble this salad at serving time, because an enzyme in kiwi, actinidin, quickly starts to break down any protein it happens to be in contact with. If the chicken and kiwi sit too long, the chicken begins to get mushy, so eat this spicy and refreshing salad while the chicken is still warm.

287 calories per serving

4 green onions, thinly sliced		
3 cloves garlic, minced		
1 ¼ tsp	dried thyme	6 mL
¾ tsp	ground allspice	4 mL
¼ tsp	salt	1 mL
Pepper, to taste		
4 tbsp	red wine vinegar, divided	60mL
2 tbsp	Dijon mustard, divided	30 mL
2 tsp	dark brown sugar	10 mL
1 pound	skinless, boneless chicken breasts	500 g
1 tbsp	olive oil	15 mL
2 cups	pineapple chunks	500 mL
4 kiwis, peeled and cut into wedges		
1 large red pepper, cut into matchsticks		
1 cup	jicama matchsticks	250 ml

1 In a large bowl, stir together half the green onions, the garlic, thyme, black pepper, allspice, and ⅛ tsp (1 mL) of the salt. Stir in 2 tbsp (30 mL) of the vinegar, 1 tbsp (15 mL) of the mustard, and the brown sugar; mix well. Add the chicken, rubbing the mixture into the chicken. Cover and set aside.

2 In a separate bowl, whisk together the remaining 2 tbsp (30 mL) vinegar, 1 tbsp (15 mL) mustard, ⅛ tsp (1 mL) salt, and the oil. Add the remaining green onions, the pineapple, kiwis, pepper, and jicama; toss to combine.

3 Preheat the broiler. Broil the chicken 6 inches (15 cm) from the heat for 4 minutes per side, or until cooked through. When cool enough to handle, slice the chicken on the diagonal. Add to the bowl and toss.

PER SERVING: 28 g protein, 6 g total fat, 1 g saturated fat, 66 mg cholesterol, 31 g carbohydrates, 5.9 g fibre.

SHOPPING

Jica-what?

Jicama is a slightly sweet, crunchy root vegetable that has been described as having a taste somewhere between a water chestnut and an apple. It can be found in any Chinese grocery store as well as in some large supermarkets and fruit and vegetable markets. If you can't find any, try using radishes, water chestnuts or celery or, if you prefer a sweeter touch, a Granny Smith apple or Asian pear.

SHRIMP, MELON & MANGO SALAD

SERVES 6

This salad combines shrimp with juicy fruits tossed in a light dressing flavoured with honey and fresh mint. The shrimp is left to marinate in the dressing so the flavours develop and infuse. This dish is perfect for a light summer meal out on the patio with a glass of sparkling water spiked with a squeeze of lime or lemon.

1 pound	cooked peeled large shrimp	500 g
	1 mango	
	1 honeydew melon, peeled and cubed	
	8 cherry tomatoes, halved	
3 cups	arugula leaves	750 mL
	1 medium cucumber, sliced	
	Salt and pepper, to taste	
	DRESSING	
2 tbsp	olive oil	30 mL
	Juice of 1 lemon	
1 tbsp	honey	15 mL
2 tbsp	chopped fresh mint	30 mL
	GARNISH	
	Fresh mint leaves	

242 calories per serving

1 Whisk together all the ingredients for the dressing in a large bowl and season lightly with salt and pepper. Add the shrimp to the dressing, cover and let marinate in the refrigerator for 30 minutes to 1 hour.

2 Halve the mango lengthwise, cutting down each side of the pit. Cut the flesh on each half in a criss-cross fashion to make cubes, then cut the cubes away from the skin.

3 Remove the shrimp from the fridge. Add the mango, melon, and tomatoes and gently stir together. Arrange the arugula leaves and cucumber slices around the edge of a shallow serving dish, and spoon the shrimp mixture into the centre. Garnish with sprigs of mint and serve. If serving for company, you can dress up the dish by spooning the salad into halved honeydew or cantaloupe melon shells.

PER SERVING: 18 g protein, 6 g total fat, 1 g saturated fat, 147 mg cholesterol, 33 g carbohydrates, 3 g fibre.

SWAP IT OUT!

● ● ● Try mixed seafood instead of the shrimp.

● ● ● To add a slightly spicy note, add 1 (1-inch/2.5-cm) slice of fresh ginger, cut into very fine strips, to the dressing.

● ● ● To vary the dressing, use the juice of 1 orange in place of the lemon juice and 2 tbsp (30 mL) of chopped fresh cilantro instead of mint.

FRUIT COMBOS
Other fruits can be used in place of the melon and mango. Good combinations include chopped nectarine and halved, seedless white grapes, or sliced kiwi with cubes of fresh pineapple.

SWAP & DROP

GOOD

341 *calories*

BETTER

219 *calories*

CRAB & AVOCADO SALAD

SERVES 6

12 ounces/375 g fresh white crabmeat

2 avocados

2 crisp green apples

½ cup/125 mL bean sprouts

3 tbsp/45 mL light mayonnaise

3 tbsp/45 mL plain low-fat yogurt

Juice from 1 lemon

Pinch cayenne pepper

1 head lettuce

¼ cup/60 mL chopped toasted walnut halves

1 cup/250 mL bulgur wheat

2 ½ cups/625 mL boiling water

1 tbsp/15 mL olive oil

3 tbsp/45 mL lemon juice

1 tbsp/15 mL snipped fresh chives

2 medium tomatoes, diced

Salt and pepper, to taste

1 Boil water in a large saucepan, then add bulgur and simmer until grains are just tender (10 to 15 minutes). Drain in a large sieve, pressing to squeeze out excess water. Combine oil, lemon juice, chives, and diced tomatoes in large mixing bowl. Add bulgur and mix; add salt and pepper to taste.

2 For crab salad: pick over and flake crabmeat, discarding shell fragments. Halve, pit, and peel avocados, then chop and add to crab. Core and thinly slice apples. Add to crabmeat with sprouts.

3 Mix mayonnaise, yogurt, lemon juice, and cayenne. Spoon onto the crab mixture and toss very gently until just combined. Place lettuce on piles of bulgur. Add crab salad; top with walnuts.

PER SERVING: 18 g protein, 15 g total fat, 2 g saturated fat, 57 mg cholesterol, 39 g carbohydrates, 10 g fibre.

LOBSTER SALAD WITH LIME DRESSING

SERVES 4

½ pound/250 g baby red-skinned new potatoes, scrubbed

2 tbsp/30 mL light mayonnaise

2 tbsp/30 mL low-fat yogurt

Finely grated zest of 1 lime

2 small shallots, thinly sliced

½ cup/125 mL snow peas, sliced

½ cup/125 mL halved seedless red grapes

½ cup/125 mL halved seedless green grapes

1 cup/250 mL watercress

2 cups/500 mL arugula lettuce

Salt and pepper, to taste

1 pound/500 g cooked lobster meat

1 Put the potatoes in a saucepan and cover with boiling water. Cook until just tender, about 15 minutes. Drain and let cool, then cut the potatoes in half.

2 While the potatoes are cooling, mix together the mayonnaise, yogurt, and lime zest, and season with salt and pepper to taste. Set aside.

3 Toss the potatoes with the shallots, snow peas, grapes, and lime dressing. Arrange the arugula on large plates and add the watercress and potato salad. Scatter the lobster meat on top and serve.

PER SERVING: 26 g protein, 2 g total fat, 0 g saturated fat, 81 mg cholesterol, 25 g carbohydrates, 2 g fibre.

TUNA, RED CABBAGE, GREEN BEAN & CAPER SALAD

SERVES 4

Crunch plus a satisfying balance of flavours makes this pretty salad a favourite.

1 cup	trimmed and diagonally sliced green beans	250 mL
4 cups	chopped red cabbage	1 L
½ cup	chopped red onion	125 mL
½ cup	chopped flat-leaf parsley	125 mL
1 6 ½-ounce	can water-packed tuna, flaked	1 184-g
2 tbsp	red-wine vinegar	30 mL
1 tbsp	extra-virgin olive oil	15 mL
1 tbsp	capers, rinsed and drained	15 mL
⅛ tsp	freshly ground black pepper	0.5 mL

162 calories per serving

1 Heat a small saucepan half-filled with water to boiling. Add the beans and cook until crisp-tender, about 3 minutes. Drain and rinse with cold water. Pat dry with paper towels.

2 Toss the beans in a large serving bowl with the cabbage, onions, parsley, tuna, vinegar, oil, capers, and pepper.

PER SERVING: 14 g protein, 8 g total fat, 1 g saturated fat, 14 mg cholesterol, 11 g carbohydrates, 3 g fibre.

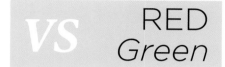

VS RED *Green*

Red cabbage has about double the vitamin C of green. Its colour is a sign of its anthocyanin content, which gives red cabbage signifi-cantly more protective phytonutri-ents. Both are rich in fibre and, to be their most nutritious, are best cooked by stovetop steaming.

GRILLED SALMON SALAD

SERVES 4

Conjure up the taste of a tropical island excursion with this unusual warm salad. The rich flavour of salmon is perfectly balanced by the gentle acidity of orange and the sweetness of mango and papaya. Serve with an accompanying salad of mixed long-grain and wild rice, or a piece of crusty French bread.

313 calories per serving

	8 cardamom pods, crushed	
1 tsp	cumin seeds	5 mL
	Finely grated zest and juice of 1 lime	
	Juice of 1 large orange	
1 tbsp	light soy sauce	15 mL
1 tbsp	honey	15 mL
4 4-ounce	pieces of skinless salmon fillet	4 125-g
4 cups	romaine or mixed salad leaves (such as oak leaf, red leaf lettuce, baby chard)	1 L
	1 mango, peeled and cut into 1-inch (2.5-cm) cubes	
	1 papaya, peeled, seeded and cut into 1-inch (2.5-cm) cubes	
	1 orange, peeled and segmented	
	Salt and pepper, to taste	

1 Heat a small non-stick frying pan over medium heat. Scrape the seeds from the cardamom pods, and add them to the hot pan with the cumin seeds. Toast for a few seconds to release the aromas, and remove the seeds to a shallow non-metallic dish.

2 Add the lime zest and juice, orange juice, soy sauce, and honey to the seeds, and season lightly with salt and pepper. Lay the pieces of salmon in the dish. Turn them over to coat both sides. Cover and let marinate for about 30 minutes.

3 Preheat a grill pan or oven broiler. Lift the salmon out of the marinade, place on a grill pan or broiler pan, and grill or broil for 4 to 5 minutes on one side only; the salmon fillets should still be slightly translucent in the centre. Meanwhile, pour the marinade into a small saucepan and bring just to a boil.

4 Arrange the salad leaves in the middle of 4 plates. Scatter the mango and papaya cubes and orange segments over the salad. Place the cooked salmon on top of the salad and drizzle with the warm marinade. Serve at once.

PER SERVING: 26 g protein, 10 g total fat, 2 g saturated fat, 77 mg cholesterol, 30 g carbohydrates, 4 g fibre.

SWAP IT OUT!

● ● ● **Asian-Style Halibut Salad**
Use 4 (4-ounce/125-g) pieces of skinless halibut fillet instead of the salmon. Make a marinade with 2 garlic cloves, crushed, 1 tsp (5 mL) grated ginger, 1 tsp (5 mL) ground cumin, 1 tsp (5 mL) ground coriander, 2 tbsp (30 mL) rice wine or dry sherry, 1 tbsp (15 mL) fish sauce, the grated zest of 1 lime, the juice of 2 limes, and salt to taste. Marinate the halibut for at least 30 minutes, then grill for 5 to 6 minutes. Strain the marinade and bring just to a boil. Serve the fish on a crunchy salad of bean sprouts, shredded Chinese (napa) cabbage, carrot, red pepper, and thinly sliced mushrooms. Drizzle the warm marinade on top.

salad dressings

When it comes to salads, a little oil is a good thing. Really! A small amount of the right oil (such as olive or canola) helps deliver the fat-soluble nutrients and vitamins in vegetables to your body. They include beta-carotene, which converts in the body to vitamin A (carrots, sweet potatoes, winter squash, leafy greens), vitamin E (leafy greens), and vitamin K (leafy greens again!). Just use a light hand, even with these calorie-wise dressings!

LEMON & BASIL DRESSING

This is particularly good on grilled vegetables.

2 tbsp	freshly squeezed lemon juice	30 mL
2 tbsp	extra virgin olive oil	30 mL
	16 fresh basil leaves, torn into pieces	
	1 garlic clove, very finely chopped	
	Pepper to taste	

Whisk together and serve.

MINT & HONEY DRESSING

This is a good dressing for shrimp; you can also use it as a 30-minute shrimp marinade.

2 tbsp	extra virgin olive oil	30 mL
2 tbsp	lemon juice	30 mL
1 tbsp	clear honey	15 mL
2 tbsp	chopped fresh mint	30 mL
	Pepper to taste	

Whisk together and serve.

ROASTED GARLIC-BUTTERMILK RANCH DRESSING

Use this as you would any creamy salad dressing. It can be made several days in advance and refrigerated until serving time.

3 ounce	bulb garlic	85 g
2 tsp	grated lemon zest	10 mL
1 tbsp	fresh lemon juice	15 mL
1 tbsp	olive oil	15 mL
1 tsp	onion powder	5 mL
¼ tsp	salt	1 mL
⅛ tsp	cayenne pepper	0.5 mL
1 cup	buttermilk	250 mL

Preheat the oven to 400°F (200°C). Wrap the garlic bulb in foil and roast for 45 minutes, or until the packet is soft to the touch. Cut off the top of the garlic bulb and squeeze the garlic pulp into a medium bowl. Whisk in the lemon zest, lemon juice, oil, onion powder, salt, and cayenne until smooth. Whisk in the buttermilk. Keep refrigerated until serving time.

PAPRIKA SOUR CREAM DRESSING

7 ounces	light sour cream	200 g
1 tbsp	vegetable oil	15 mL
2 tbsp	water	30 mL
2 tbsp	herb vinegar	30 mL
	Freshly ground black pepper, to taste	
¼ tsp	ground sweet paprika	1 mL

Mix until creamy.

TOMATO VINAIGRETTE

Excellent with a mixture of lettuce and tomatoes.

	2 large tomatoes	
2 tbsp	olive oil	30 mL
1 tbsp	champagne vinegar	15 mL
2 tbsp	lemon juice	30 mL
	4 sprigs fresh thyme, finely chopped	
	Salt, ground pepper to taste	

Whisk oil, champagne vinegar, lemon juice, and thyme until combined; add salt and pepper to taste.

YOGURT DRESSING

The perfect topper for when you want to add a few shrimp to your lettuce.

1 cup	yogurt	250 g
2 tbsp	low-fat mayonnaise	30 mL
1 tsp	dry vermouth	5 mL
1 tbsp	lime juice	15 mL
	Pinch of cayenne pepper	
	Salt, pepper to taste.	

Stir first four ingredients until creamy. Season to taste.

RASPBERRY NUT DRESSING

This herb vinaigrette complements bitter radicchio or peppery arugula. Vary the herbs to match different salads.

2 tsp	hazelnut oil	10 mL
3 tbsp	canola or peanut oil	45 mL
2 tbsp	raspberry or other fruit vinegar	30 mL
1 tbsp	Dijon mustard	15 mL
	Salt, ground white pepper to taste	
	2 green onions, finely chopped	
	4 sprigs each fresh parsley, tarragon, basil, and dill	

Whisk the two oils with the vinegar, mustard, salt, and pepper. Add spring onions and finely chopped leaves of all the herbs.

RASPBERRY VINEGAR

1 pound	fresh or frozen raspberries	500 g
2 cups	white wine vinegar	500 mL
1 ½ cups	sugar	375 mL

Crush raspberries. Add vinegar and let sit overnight. Press through a sieve into a jar. Add sugar; still until dissolved. Refrigerate or store in a cool, dark place. Keeps for up to two weeks.

Super salad SWAPS

Love grandma's sour cream dressing? Try lightening up your high-fat favourites by swapping in low-fat alternatives. Use low-fat sour cream and mayo, or go one better nutritionally by trying **PLAIN YOGURT** with or without a shot of buttermilk, cottage cheese, or puréed avocado.

Try swapping some of all of the oil in dressing recipes with an extra acidic hit: **TOMATO JUICE, APPLE JUICE, CITRUS JUICE**. Or add a little water to your dressing recipe, which stretches the oil. If the extra liquids prevent your dressing from becoming emulsified, try adding a bit of prepared mustard, like Dijon.

Eliminate oil-based dressing entirely by using **SALSA**, a highly flavoured substitute that makes veggies sing olé! Or dress your salad with a chopped, hard-boiled egg, a nice change of pace that helps you feel fuller longer by virtue of its high protein content.

Experiment with **FLAVOURED OILS**, which can be strong enough to reduce the amount needed, and premium vinegars, which can be so smooth that you might be tempted to eliminate oil entirely.

No time for homemade? Try **SPRITZERS**; at 1 calorie per spray, it can take just 10 calories to coat your entire salad.

SHRED, BABY, SHRED
Chopping your lettuce and other veggies into smaller pieces create, fewer nooks and crannies for dressing to cling and pool.

FRESH ORANGE DRESSING

Try this on romaine; add some chicken if you like.

½ tsp	finely grated orange rind	2 mL
1 tbsp	freshly squeezed orange juice	15 mL
1 tsp	Dijon mustard	5 mL
2 tbsp	sunflower oil	30 mL
1 tbsp	walnut oil	30 mL
	Pepper to taste	

Whisk together until slightly thickened.

CURRY DRESSING

Use this instead of mayonnaise for a nice change to chicken salad.

⅔ cup	plain low-fat yogurt	150 g
5 tbsp	reduced-fat mayonnaise	75 mL
2 tbsp	korma curry paste	30 mL
	Grated rind of 1 large lemon	
1 tbsp	freshly squeezed lemon juice, or to taste	15 mL
2 tbsp	snipped fresh chives	30 mL
2 tbsp	chopped fresh mint	30 mL
2 tbsp	chopped parsley	30 mL
	Pepper to taste	

Mix the yogurt, mayonnaise, curry paste, and lemon rind and juice until well blended. Stir in the chives, mint, parsley, and pepper.

WASABI-MISO DRESSING

Wasabi is a type of horseradish found in paste or powder in Asian food markets or in the international section of the supermarket. Once opened, refrigerate. Serve this spicy dressing on mixed greens, sliced cucumbers, or in chicken salad.

2 tbsp	wasabi powder	30 mL
2 tbsp	yellow shiro miso paste	30 mL
¼ cup	fresh lime juice	60 mL
1 tbsp	dark sesame oil	15 mL
1 tbsp	honey	15 mL
¼ tsp	salt	1 mL
½ tsp	ground ginger	2 mL

In a large bowl, stir together the wasabi powder and 2 tbsp of water to form a paste. Stir in the miso. Whisk in the lime juice, sesame oil, honey, salt, and ginger until smooth.

TARRAGON VINAIGRETTE

3 tbsp	olive oil	45 mL
2 tbsp	white wine vinegar	30 mL
2 tsp	finely chopped tarragon	10 mL
1 tsp	Dijon mustard	5 mL
1 tsp	honey	5 mL
	1 clove garlic, crushed	
	Salt, freshly ground black pepper to taste	

Whisk together and serve.

CHILI LIME DRESSING

This dressing works beautifully with cooling cucumber, tart kiwi, and sweet, peppery mango. Boost the flavour by marinating 1 medium onion, sliced, in the dressing for 30 minutes.

	1 fresh red chili pepper, seeded and finely chopped	
2 tbsp	olive oil	30 mL
2 tbsp	lime juice	30 mL
1 tsp	clear honey	5 mL
2 tbsp	chopped fresh cilantro	30 mL
	Salt and freshly ground black pepper	

Whisk together and serve.

OLIVE VINAIGRETTE

1 tbsp	olive oil	15 mL
1 tbsp	balsamic vinegar	15 mL
1 tbsp	lemon juice	15 mL
	2 cloves garlic, finely chopped	
	15 each pitted green and black olives, finely chopped	
½ tsp	dried thyme	2 mL
½ tsp	dried oregano	2 mL
	Salt, ground black pepper to taste	

Whisk together oil, vinegar, lemon juice, and garlic. Fold in olives, herbs; stir in salt and pepper.

HONEY MUSTARD DRESSING

Perfect when tossed with leaf lettuces and, if it's blueberry season, throw in a generous handful.

3 tbsp	sunflower oil	45 mL
	Juice of 1 lemon	
1 tsp	Dijon mustard	5 mL
1 tsp	honey	5 mL
	Salt and pepper, to taste.	

Whisk together and serve.

BASIL BUTTERMILK DRESSING

For a change of pace, try different herbs and herb combinations.

1 cup	buttermilk	250 mL
1 cup	low-fat sour cream	250 mL
¼ cup plus 2 tsp	grated Parmesan	60mL plus 10 mL
½ tsp	onion salt	2 mL
	1 garlic cloves, minced	
3 tbsp	fresh basil, minced	45 mL

Or try this super-speedy buttermilk dressing:

¾ cup	buttermilk	175 mL
2 cups	low-fat cottage cheese	500 mL
	1 envelope ranch dressing mix	

Combine and refrigerate for at least 1 hour.

 SHAKE THINGS UP!

Get rid of glops of creamy dressing clinging to crisp romaine, or greens swimming in a puddle of Italian. Slash dressing consumption without changing ingredients by snapping a lid on the serving bowl and gently shaking until the veggies are coated. Start with half your usual amount of dressing and, if necessary, add extra in dribs and drabs. Take your time; the method calls for a bit of patience.

HOLD-THE-OIL FRENCH DRESSING

⅓ cup	sugar	75 mL
⅓ cup	cider vinegar	75 mL
1 tbsp	Worcestershire sauce	15 mL
1 tbsp	onion, grated	15 mL
	salt, pepper to taste	
½ tsp	ground mustard	2 mL
	1 garlic clover, minced	
½ tsp	paprika	2 mL

Whisk until blended.

soups & sandwiches

Soup and a sandwich are a classic, comforting duo, but watch for the combined calorie count if you're sitting down to enjoy the pair together. If you just can't resist, consider making it your main meal, fix yourself half a sandwich, or trim the protein portion and pile on a few extra veggies.

SPICED CREAM OF BUTTERNUT SQUASH SOUP   SERVES 4

Curry powder and ginger lend a decidedly Indian feel to this nutrient-packed soup. Not only is it soothing, but it also provides a hefty amount of beta-carotene as well as potassium, calcium, and magnesium.

2 tsp	olive oil	10 mL
	1 large onion, finely chopped	
	4 red apples	
2 pounds	butternut squash, peeled and thinly sliced	1 kg
	1 large baking potato, peeled and thinly sliced	
2 tsp	curry powder	10 mL
1 tsp	ground ginger	5 mL
¼ tsp	salt	1 mL
½ tsp	cinnamon	2 mL
1 cup	low-fat (1%) milk	250 mL
¼ cup	roasted cashews, coarsely chopped	60 mL

314 calories per serving

1 In a large saucepan, heat the oil over medium heat. Add the onion, and cook, stirring frequently for 5 minutes, or until golden brown.

2 Peel, core, and slice 3 ½ of the apples. Add to the saucepan along with the butternut squash, potato, curry powder, ginger, salt, and cinnamon, and stir to combine. Add 3 cups of water; cover and simmer for 30 minutes, or until the squash is tender.

3 Transfer to a food processor and process until smooth. Return the mixture to the pan, add the milk, and whisk to combine. Cook over low heat until heated through.

4 Meanwhile, thinly slice the remaining half apple (unpeeled). Spoon the soup into 4 mugs or soup bowls and top with the cashews and apple slices.

PER SERVING: 7 g protein, 7.7 g total fat, 1.5 g saturated fat, 2 mg cholesterol, 61 g carbohydrates, 8 g fibre.

CHICKEN-KALE SOUP & ROASTED PEPPER PURÉE SERVES 4

Nutty-flavoured flaxseed oil, a source of omega-3, is available in the refrigerated section of many health-food stores. If you can't find it, substitute dark sesame oil.

1 pound	skinless, boneless chicken thighs, cut into 2.5-cm (1-in.) chunks	500 g
	4 carrots, thinly sliced	
	3 large red onions, cut into 1/2-inch (1-cm) chunks	
	5 cloves garlic, minced, plus 1 whole clove garlic	
2 tbsp	finely chopped fresh ginger	30 mL
1 tsp	cayenne pepper	5 mL
I tsp	salt	5 mL
	2 red peppers, cut lengthwise into 2 flat panels	
1 tbsp	hulled roasted pumpkin seeds	15 mL
1 tbsp	flaxseed oil	15 mL
½ cup	orzo pasta	125 mL
8 cups	shredded kale	2L

433 calories per serving

1 In a large stockpot, combine 4 cups (1 L) of water, the chicken, carrots, onions, minced garlic, ginger, cayenne, and salt; bring to a boil over high heat. Reduce to a simmer; partially cover and cook for 25 minutes.

2 Turn on the over broiler. Place the pepper pieces, skin side up, on a cookie sheet and broil 15 cm (6 inches) from the heat for 10 minutes, or until the skin is well charred. When cool enough to handle, peel the peppers and transfer them to a food processor along with the pumpkin seeds, flaxseed oil, and whole garlic clove; process until puréed.

3 Add orzo to the soup, and cook, uncovered, for 5 minutes. Stir in kale, and cook for 5 minutes, or until kale and orzo are tender. Serve the soup garnished with the roasted pepper purée.

PER SERVING: 38 g protein, 12 g total fat, 2 g saturated fat, 118 mg cholesterol, 48 g carbohydrates, 9 g fibre.

SEED NEED
Besides adding a bit of welcome bit of crunch, **pumpkin seeds are rich in monounsaturated fatty acids** (MUFA), like oleic acid, that helps lower bad LDL cholesterol and increase good HDL cholesterol. They're yummy tossed on your salad, dotted on your muffin tops, or swapped in for pine nuts in pesto.

ASPARAGUS SOUP

SERVES 6

Asparagus is an excellent source of folate, a B vitamin that helps in preventing heart disease and, when consumed by pregnant women, birth defects.

2 pounds	asparagus, trimmed	1 kg
1 tbsp	canola oil	15 mL
1 tsp	butter	5 mL
2 medium leeks, pale green and white parts only, rinsed and finely chopped		
1 small onion, finely chopped		
2 cloves garlic, crushed		
3 tbsp	uncooked long-grain white rice	45 mL
Grated zest of 1 lemon		
5 cups	low-sodium chicken stock	1.25 L
½ tsp	dried tarragon	2 mL
3 tbsp	plain yogurt	45 mL
Salt, pepper to taste		

111 calories per serving

1 Slice the tips from the asparagus; blanch in boiling water for 1 minute. Drain. Coarsely chop remaining asparagus.

2 Heat oil and butter in a large saucepan over medium heat. Add leeks, onion and garlic; sauté until softened, 5 minutes. Add chopped asparagus. Cook, covered, for 10 minutes.

3 Add rice, lemon zest, stock, salt, and pepper. Partially cover; simmer for 30 minutes.

4 Purée soup in batches in a blender or food processor. Return to pan. Stir in tarragon and the reserved asparagus tips. Simmer 3 minutes. Remove from heat. Stir in yogurt and serve.

PER SERVING: 6 g protein, 4 g total fat, 1 g saturated fat, 2 mg cholesterol, 15 g carbohydrates, 2 g fibre.

:) DYNAMIC DUO

Pair this rich-tasting soup with poached fish and white wine for a luscious luncheon or light supper. You also get unexpected benefits; Italian researchers recently found that women who consumed as little as one glass of wine a day had higher blood levels of the omega-3 fats found in fish such as trout, salmon, and sardines. Beer and spirits fell flat. Furthermore, scientists believe that antioxidants in wine might be responsible for an improvement in omega-3 absorption.

KEEP IT CRISP
Store fresh-bought asparagus upright in the fridge, in enough water to keep the bottom of the stems wet.

SWAP & DROP

GOOD

302 *calories*

BETTER

88 *calories*

MUSHROOM & WINTER VEGETABLE SOUP — SERVES 4

- ½ cup/125 mL dried shiitake mushrooms
- 1 ½ cups/375 mL boiling water
- 2 tbsp/30 mL olive oil
- 1 large onion, finely chopped
- 4 cloves garlic, minced
- 1 large carrot, thinly sliced
- 1 large parsnip (about 8 ounces/230 g), thinly sliced
- 1 small head green cabbage (1 ½ pound/700 g), shredded
- 1 ¼ cups/300 mL frozen baby lima beans
- ⅓ cup/75 mL chopped fresh dill
- ⅓ cup/75 mL tomato paste
- ¼ cup/60 mL red wine vinegar
- Salt, to taste

1 In a small bowl, combine the shiitake mushrooms and boiling water. Let stand for 20 minutes, or until softened. Remove the mushrooms. Strain the reserved liquid through a fine-meshed sieve or coffee filter; set aside. Trim the mushroom stems and coarsely chop the caps.

2 In a large pot or Dutch oven, heat the oil over medium heat. Add the onion and garlic, cook for 5 minutes, or until the onion is light golden. Add the carrot and parsnip, cook for 5 minutes, or until the carrot is crisp-tender.

3 Stir in the cabbage. Cover and cook for 5 minutes, or until the cabbage begins to wilt. Stir in the mushrooms and reserved liquid, lima beans, dill, tomato paste, vinegar, salt, and 3 cups (750 mL) of water; bring to a boil. Reduce to a simmer; cover, and cook for 25 minutes, or until the soup is richly flavoured.

PER SERVING: 9 g protein, 8 g total fat, 1 g saturated fat, 0 mg cholesterol, 48 g carbohydrates, 13 g fibre.

SUMMER GARDEN SOUP — SERVES 6

- 2 tsp/10 mL olive oil
- 1 medium onion, finely chopped
- 1 large stalk celery, finely chopped
- 2 tsp /10 mL peeled, finely chopped fresh ginger
- ¼ pound/125 g green beans, cut into short pieces
- 2 medium potatoes, unpeeled, cut into small cubes
- 1 large carrot, peeled and cubed
- 1 medium yellow summer squash, quartered lengthwise, seeded and cubed
- 1 bay leaf
- ¼ tsp/1 mL salt
- ¾ cup/180 mL fresh or frozen green peas
- 2 plum tomatoes, seeded and coarsely chopped
- 2 tbsp/30 mL finely chopped basil leaves
- 1 ½ tsp/12 mL finely chopped thyme leaves

1 Heat oil in a large pot over medium heat. Add onion, celery, and ginger. Sauté until very tender, 10 minutes. Add green beans, potato, carrot, squash, 8 cups (2 L) water, bay leaf, and salt. Simmer, covered, 20 minutes.

2 Uncover soup. Simmer 15 minutes. For the last 5 minutes, add peas, tomato, basil, and thyme. Remove bay leaf. Serve.

PER SERVING: 3 g protein, 2 g total fat, 0 g saturated fat, 0 mg cholesterol, 17 g carbohydrates, 4 g fibre.

TURKEY, CHESTNUT & BARLEY SOUP

SERVES 8

One of the best parts of roasting a turkey is making a big pot of soup from the rest of the bird. If you're not roasting a turkey, use low-sodium canned chicken broth instead of the homemade stock. Add winter vegetables and chestnuts for a satisfying, healthy meal.

302
calories per serving

SOUP

2 pounds	cooked turkey breast (boneless)	1 kg
	3 large carrots, peeled and chopped	
	4 large white turnips, peeled and chopped	
	4 large celery stalks, chopped	
6 ounces	pearl onions, peeled	175 g
1 cup	pearl barley	250 mL
8 ounces	Brussels sprouts, halved or chopped	225 g
1 cup	coarsely chopped chestnuts	250 mL
¼ cup	chopped fresh parsley	60 mL

STOCK

1 turkey carcass (from at least a 12-pound/5.5-kg bird), or 5 pounds/2.5 kg) turkey parts, on bone
1 large yellow onion, peeled and quartered
2 large celery stalks, coarsely chopped
10 sprigs each of fresh parsley and thyme
1 large bay leaf
12 black peppercorns
Salt, pepper to taste

1 Begin by making the stock. Break up the turkey carcass, discarding any skin, and place in an 8-quart (8-L) stockpot. Add enough cold water to cover (about 12 cups/3 L), and bring to a boil over high heat; skim off any foam with a slotted spoon. Add the remaining ingredients for the stock and return to a full boil.

2 Lower the heat and simmer the stock gently, uncovered, for 1 ½ hours. Strain and discard the bones and vegetables (you need 9 cups/2.5 L of stock). Skim off any fat and return the stock to the stockpot.

3 To make the soup, return the stock to a boil. Remove the skin from the turkey breast and cut the turkey into bite-sized pieces (you need 6 cups/1.5 L). Add the turkey to the stockpot along with the carrots, turnips, celery, onions, and barley. Simmer the soup, uncovered, until the barley is tender, about 30 minutes.

4 Add the Brussels sprouts and chestnuts and simmer just until the sprouts are crisp-tender, about 5 minutes. Sprinkle with the parsley and serve steaming hot.

PER SERVING: 39 g protein, 2 g total fat, 0 g saturated fat, 95 mg cholesterol, 33 g carbohydrates, 6 g fibre.

BARLEY BONUS

● ● ● **Swap your bread**
Barley is a tasty addition to bread; try switching up the taste of your old favourites, like grilled cheese, with bread made with barley, spelt, or oats.

● ● ● **Make your own granola!**
Combine equal amounts of barley and spelt flakes with rolled oats. Mix in chopped walnuts and drizzle with honey or maple syrup. Place on a cookie sheet and bake until golden, stirring occasionally.

CHICKEN & FRESH CORN CHOWDER

SERVES 6

Here's a chowder that tastes rich and creamy, but is made with low-fat milk instead of cream. Use fresh corn and flavour with fresh tarragon and black pepper. Crumbled turkey bacon can be used as a garnish instead of incorporating it into the soup. Serve with a crisp vegetable salad.

357 calories per serving

INGREDIENT INTEL

Turkey bacon is lower in fat than pork bacon and can be substituted in any recipe. The sodium content of the turkey bacon is still high, however, so it should be used in moderation in your diet.

Corn contains some protein, but it is an incomplete protein because it lacks two essential amino acids (tryptophan and lysine). When eaten with beans or other legumes, it provides a complete protein.

CHOWDER		
	4 large ears yellow corn on the cob	
2 tsp	canola oil	10 mL
	1 large onion, finely chopped	
	2 large potatoes, peeled and cut into ½-inch (1-cm) chunks	
2 ½ cups	reduced-sodium chicken broth	625 mL
2 cups	1% milk	500 mL
1 pound	cooked boneless, skinless chicken breasts, cut into bite-sized pieces	500 g
2 tsp	chopped fresh tarragon or	10 mL
½ tsp	dried tarragon	2 mL
¼ tsp	freshly ground black pepper	1 mL
GARNISH		
	4 slices turkey bacon	
	Fresh tarragon leaves	

1 Remove the green husks and all the silk from the corn. Stand each cob on the wide stem end on a chopping board, at an angle. Cut the corn kernels off the cob with a serrated knife (you need 2 cups/500 mL kernels). Set aside.

2 Heat the oil in a large saucepan over medium-high heat. Add the onion and sauté until tender, but not brown, about 5 minutes. Stir in the potatoes and corn kernels and cook 5 minutes, stirring frequently. Pour in the chicken broth and bring to a boil. Lower the heat to medium-low and simmer gently until the potatoes are tender, but not breaking apart, about 5 minutes.

3 Stir in the milk, one-third of the chicken, the chopped tarragon, and pepper. Cook, stirring gently, until hot, about 3 minutes.

4 Pour one-third of the mixture into a food processor or blender and blend to a coarse texture, not to a purée. Return to the pan. Stir in the rest of the chicken and heat the chowder until hot.

5 In a medium skillet, cook the bacon over medium-high heat until golden brown and crisp. Drain on paper towels, then crumble. Ladle the chowder into 6 bowls. Sprinkle each bowl with one-quarter of the bacon and a few tarragon leaves. Serve steaming hot.

PER SERVING: 3 g protein, 2 g total fat, 0 g saturated fat, 0 mg cholesterol, 17 g carbohydrates, 4 g fibre.

MANHATTAN SHRIMP CHOWDER

SERVES 4

Shrimp are served to delicious effect in a classic Manhattan-style chowder, minus the usual bacon. Toss a can of clams in for seafood chowder.

2 tsp	olive oil	10 mL
	1 medium onion, finely chopped	
	4 garlic cloves, minced	
12 ounces	potatoes, cut into ½-inch (1.5-cm) dice	350 g
1 cup	bottled clam juice	250 mL
½ tsp	fennel seed	2 mL
1 tsp	grated orange zest	5 mL
1 14 ½-ounce	can stewed tomatoes, chopped	1 400-g
⅛ tsp	salt	0.5 mL
½ tsp	hot red pepper sauce	2 mL
8 ounces	medium shrimp, peeled, deveined and cut into bite-size pieces	225 g
½ cup	frozen whole-kernel corn	125 mL

240 calories per serving

1 Heat oil in a large nonstick saucepan over medium heat. Add onion and garlic and sauté for 7 minutes or until onion is softened.

2 Stir in potatoes, clam juice, 1 cup (250 mL) water, fennel seed, and orange zest. Bring to boil. Reduce to simmer, cover, and cook 10 minutes or until potatoes are almost tender.

3 Stir in tomatoes, salt, and hot pepper sauce. Return to boil. Add shrimp and corn. Cover and cook 3 minutes or until shrimp are just opaque and corn is hot.

PER SERVING: 17 g protein, 2 g total fat, 0 g saturated fat, 130 mg cholesterol, 30 g carbohydrates, 5 g fibre.

VS FRESH *Frozen, Canned*

Fresh isn't always the best for fruits and vegetables, especially if they take a long time to get to market. Both frozen and canned are good options, packed with nutrients due to swift processing. If choosing canned, just make sure you rinse off the packing water!

GRILLED EGGPLANT & TOMATO SANDWICH

This blend of Mediterranean crops, meltingly layered with tangy goat cheese and fried until golden brown, elevates the lowly grilled cheese.

133 calories per serving

2 ounces	goat cheese, crumbled	60 g
1 tbsp	snipped fresh chives	15 mL
¼ cup	dry bread crumbs	60 mL
2 tbsp	grated Parmesan cheese	30 mL
½ tsp	dried basil	2 mL
	1 large egg	
	1 large egg white	
¼ tsp	salt	1 mL
	12 slices peeled eggplant, ¼ inch (5 mm) thick	
	6 thin slices tomato, blotted dry	
2 tbsp	olive oil	30 mL

1 Combine goat cheese and chives in a small bowl. Combine bread crumbs, Parmesan, and basil in a shallow dish. Beat egg, egg white, and salt in a second shallow dish.

2 Spread about 2 tsp (10 mL) goat cheese mixture onto a slice of eggplant. Top with a tomato slice and an eggplant slice. Make 5 more sandwiches the same way.

3 Dip each sandwich in egg mixture, then bread crumb mixture to coat both sides. Place on wax paper.

4 In large non-stick frying pan over medium-low heat, heat about 1 ½ tbsp (20 mL) oil. Add sandwiches in a single layer, working in batches if necessary. Cook until fork-tender and golden brown, 10 to 12 minutes, turning over halfway through cooking. Add more oil as needed if pan becomes dry. Serve warm.

PER SERVING: 6 g protein, 10 g total fat, 4 g saturated fat, 47 mg cholesterol, 6 g carbohydrates,1 g fibre.

MUSHROOM & THYME TOASTS

Prepare these for a satisfying snack or a quick lunch paired with fresh fruit. The smooth flavour of the mushrooms is enhanced by cooking them with garlic, herbs, and a dollop of tangy, low-fat sour cream. The mushrooms taste wonderful piled on top of whole-grain toast spread with light ricotta cheese.

148 calories per serving

½ cup	light ricotta cheese	125 mL
	2 celery stalks, finely chopped	
3 tbsp	finely chopped parsley	45 mL
	Good pinch of cayenne pepper	
1 pound	mushrooms	500 g
	1 garlic clove, crushed	
2 tbsp	chopped fresh thyme	30 mL
2 tbsp	low-fat sour cream	30 mL
1 tsp	lemon juice	5 mL
	Salt and pepper, to taste	
	8 slices (1 inch/2.5 cm) cut from a small loaf of whole-grain bread	

1 Place the ricotta, celery, parsley, and cayenne pepper in a bowl and mix well.

2 Leave any small mushrooms whole and halve larger ones. Place them in a large, heavy, non-stick frying pan and add the garlic, thyme, sour cream, and 1 tsp (5 mL) water. Cover and cook gently until the mushrooms are just tender and have given up their juices, about 3 to 4 minutes. Add the lemon juice and season lightly with salt and pepper.

3 While the mushrooms are cooking, toast the bread slices on both sides under the broiler. While still warm, spread one side of each piece of toast with some of the ricotta mixture, then cut it in half.

4 Arrange the toasts on individual serving plates. Spoon on the hot mushroom mixture and serve immediately.

PER SERVING: 8 g protein, 4 g total fat, 1 g saturated fat, 6 mg cholesterol, 24 g carbohydrates, 4 g fibre.

1 MORE IDEA

● ● ● **Devilled Mushroom Toasts**

Heat 1 tbsp (15 mL) olive oil in a non-stick skillet, add 1 thinly sliced onion and cook over medium heat until softened. Stir in 1 minced garlic clove, 1 pound (500 g) halved mushrooms, and 1 seeded and diced red pepper. Cook, stirring frequently, for 2 minutes, then stir in 2 tsp (10 mL) Worcestershire sauce, 1 tsp (5 mL) Dijon mustard, and 1 tsp (5 mL) dark brown sugar. Lower the heat and cook gently for 5 minutes, stirring occasionally. Add 2 tbsp (30 mL) chopped parsley and season lightly with salt and pepper. Toast the bread and spread with ½ cup (125 mL) low-fat soft goat cheese. Spoon on hot devilled mushroom mixture and serve.

INGREDIENT INTEL
Because of its high moisture content, ricotta cheese is lower in fat than many other varieties of soft cheese.

SAUSAGE, PEPPER & TOMATO BRUSCHETTA

SERVES 10

This open sandwich of toasted ciabatta bread with a mixed pepper topping is typical of the style of food enjoyed in Mediterranean countries, where bread (along with plenty of fruit and vegetables) is a mainstay of the diet. A little chorizo adds a spicy note to the mix of peppers.

	1 ciabatta loaf or French bread	
	1 red pepper, halved and seeded	
	1 yellow pepper, halved and seeded	
2 ounces	chorizo sausage, thinly sliced	60 g
1 cup	quartered cherry tomatoes	250 mL
2 tbsp	tomato relish or chutney	30 mL
½ cup	torn fresh basil leaves	125 mL
1 tbsp	olive oil	15 mL
	1 garlic clove, minced	
	Black pepper	

150 calories per serving

INGREDIENT INTEL
Chorizo is a popular Spanish sausage made with pork and pimento, a Spanish pepper. Though chorizo has a high fat content, this can be drastically cut by using a small amount, sautéing it in a dry pan and draining it well.

1 Preheat the oven to 400°F (200°C). Wrap the bread in foil and bake for 8 to 10 minutes. Remove from the oven and place on a wire rack to cool. Preheat the oven broiler to high.

2 When the broiler is hot, place the peppers skin side up on a baking tray and broil until the flesh softens and the skin begins to blister and char, about 8 to 10 minutes. Transfer the peppers to a plastic zipper bag, seal, and set aside until cool enough to handle.

3 While the peppers are cooling, sauté the chorizo slices in a small frying pan until the oil runs out and the slices start to crisp, about 3 to 4 minutes. Drain on a paper towel.

4 Place the chorizo in a bowl and add the tomatoes, relish or chutney, and basil. Remove the cooled peppers from the bag and peel away their skins. Roughly chop the flesh and add to the bowl. Season lightly with pepper and mix well. Set aside while you prepare the toasts.

5 Cut the baked ciabatta across into 5 pieces, then cut each piece in half horizontally. Mix the olive oil and garlic and brush this mixture onto the cut sides of the ciabatta pieces. Place them cut side up under the broiler and toast until golden and crisp, about 2 to 3 minutes.

6 Top the toasted ciabatta with the pepper and chorizo mixture and serve immediately.

PER SERVING: 5 g protein, 3 g total fat, 1 g saturated fat, 3 mg cholesterol, 27 g carbohydrates, 5 g fibre.

SWAP THE TOP
For a vegetarian topping, omit the chorizo and sprinkle ¼ cup (50 mL) toasted pine nuts over the pepper and tomato mixture. Or, replace the chorizo with 2 ounces (60 g) crumbled feta or goat cheese.

SARDINE & PEPPER TOASTS

A no-cook recipe is perfect for a light lunch when time is short. Remember to include the sardine bones in the mixture, as they are quite soft and mash easily, adding valuable calcium to the dish. The raw vegetables have maximum food value to keep you going on a busy working day. Follow with some juicy fresh fruit.

208 calories per serving

2 3 ½-ounce	cans sardines, in spring water, drained	2 105-g
	2 celery stalks, finely chopped	
	1 red pepper, deseeded and finely chopped	
	1 red onion, thinly sliced	
¼ cup	tomato paste	60 g
¼ cup	lime juice	60 mL
	Pinch of celery salt	
	4 thick slices multigrain bread	
3 ounces	watercress leaves	75 g

1 Lightly break up the sardines in a bowl with a fork. Add the chopped celery, red pepper, onion, tomato paste, and lime juice to the sardines. Season lightly with celery salt and freshly ground black pepper.

2 Lightly toast the bread slices on both sides until golden. Divide the watercress leaves among the slices and spoon the sardine mixture on top. Serve immediately.

PER SERVING: 15.5 g protein, 6 g total fat, 1.5 g saturated fat, 15 mg cholesterol, 20 g carbohydrates, 5 g fibre.

SHOPPING

Watercress wisdom

When buying watercress, always buy more than you need because you will have to cut off the stems and choose only the tips of the leaves to use. If your watercress has wilted, refresh the picked leaves in a bowl of cold water, then drain well.

CHICKEN, AVOCADO & ALFALFA CLUB SANDWICH SERVES 2

This triple-decker, toasted sandwich is packed with creamy, mashed avocado, rich in healthy unsaturated fats. Lean chicken, juicy tomatoes, and pretty alfalfa sprouts make up the rest of the tasty filling for this nourishing and satisfying bite.

1 ½ tbsp	lime juice	22 mL
1 tsp	olive oil	5 mL
	½ red onion, very thinly sliced	
	½ avocado	
	Dash of Tabasco or chili sauce	
2 tbsp	97% fat-free mayonnaise	30 mL
2 tbsp	chopped fresh cilantro	30 mL
	6 slices salt-reduced whole-grain bread	
⅓ pound cooked, skinless chicken breast fillet, sliced		175 g
	2 tomatoes, thinly sliced	
¾ cup	alfalfa sprouts	25 g

546 calories per serving

1 Whisk together 2 tsp (10 mL) of the lime juice, olive oil, and a grating of pepper in a small bowl. Add the onion slices and toss to coat. Set aside to allow the onion to mellow in flavour while you prepare the remaining ingredients.

2 Roughly mash the avocado with a fork. Add remaining lime juice and Tabasco or chili sauce, to taste, and carry on mashing until mixture is fairly smooth. Mix mayonnaise with cilantro.

3 Preheat a grill pan to medium, or turn on oven broiler. Place the bread on the grill pan and toast or grill for 2 to 3 minutes on each side until lightly browned.

4 Spread 2 slices of toast very thinly with some of the mayonnaise, then spread with half the mashed avocado, dividing it equally. Top with the chicken and onion slices. Spread another two slices of toast very thinly with mayonnaise, then place over the chicken filling, mayonnaise-side down. Spread half the remaining mayonnaise thinly over the tops of the sandwiches. Spread with the remaining avocado, then add a layer of sliced tomatoes and the sprouts.

5 Finally, spread the last of the mayonnaise over the last two slices of toast and place on the sandwiches, mayonnaise-side down. Press the sandwiches together, then cut each in quarters. Serve immediately.

PER SERVING: 34.5 g protein, 23 g total fat, 5 g saturated fat, 59 mg cholesterol, 44.5 g carbohydrates, 9.5 g fibre.

SWAP IT OUT!

● ● ● Grated carrot can be used instead of the alfalfa sprouts. Bean sprouts are also a good option. Use about 1 ½ cups (50 g).

INGREDIENT INTEL
Sprouts are easy to grow yourself.
Rinse adzuki, alfalfa, or mung beans and place in a large jar. Half-fill with cold water, then cover with a piece of muslin secured with an elastic band. Leave to soak overnight, then pour off the water through the muslin. Refill the jar with fresh water, then drain and leave the jar on its side in a dark place. Repeat this process twice a day for 2 days until sprouted, then place the jar in a sunny place and continue rinsing for another day or two until the sprouts have grown to the desired size. Rinse well and discard any unsprouted beans before using.

SWAP FOR BREAD
Cooked and cooled polenta can be cut into shapes and grilled to make an excellent base for a tempting topping.

POLENTA & MUSHROOM GRILLS

SERVES 6

These polenta fingers are flavoured with Gruyère cheese, and the topping is a savoury mixture of mushrooms, walnuts, and herbs. Serve as a sophisticated appetizer—with a few mixed salad leaves, if you like.

2 ½ cups	reduced-sodium vegetable broth	625 mL
1 cup	instant polenta (cornmeal)	250 mL
½ cup	grated Gruyère cheese	125 mL
1 ounce	dried porcini mushrooms	30 g
2 tbsp	olive oil, divided	30 mL
½ pound	sliced cremini or button mushrooms	250 g
3 tbsp	dry sherry	45 mL
2 tbsp	chopped fresh flat-leaf parsley	30 mL
2 tsp	chopped fresh rosemary	10 mL
⅓ cup	finely chopped walnuts	75 mL
	Salt and pepper, to taste	
	GARNISH	
	Flat-leaf parsley	

246 calories per 2 grills

HOW TO ROAST NUTS

Roasting nuts brings out their flavour. Preheat oven to 300°F/150°C. Place shelled nuts in a single layer on a baking sheet and roast for 7 to 10 minutes. Sprinkle chopped or whole on salads, frozen low-fat yogurt, or sorbet.

1 Bring the broth to a boil in a large saucepan. Pour in the polenta in a steady stream, stirring with a wooden spoon to prevent lumps from forming. Cook on low heat, stirring constantly, for about 5 minutes or until the mixture thickens and pulls away from the sides of the saucepan. Remove from heat and stir in the Gruyère cheese. Season lightly with salt and pepper.

2 Pour the polenta onto a baking sheet coated with cooking spray and spread out into a rectangle about ½ inch (1 cm) thick. Allow to cool for 1 hour. Meanwhile, put the dried porcini mushrooms in a bowl and cover with boiling water. Let soak for 20 minutes then drain, reserving 2 tbsp (30 mL) of the soaking liquid. Finely chop the mushrooms.

3 Heat the broiler to medium-high. Lightly brush the surface of the polenta with 1 tbsp (15 mL) oil. Cut the polenta rectangle into 12 fingers, about 2 ½ inches (6 cm) long. Separate the fingers and place them on a baking sheet. Broil for 4 minutes. Turn the polenta slices over and broil for an additional 2 to 3 minutes or until lightly browned. Remove from the oven and keep hot.

4 Heat the remaining 1 tbsp (15 mL) oil in a large non-stick frying pan. Add the soaked dried mushrooms and the sliced cremini mushrooms and sauté over medium-high heat until softened, about 3 to 4 minutes.

5 Add the sherry and the reserved mushroom soaking liquid. Cook over high heat for 1 to 2 minutes, stirring, until most of the liquid has evaporated. Add the parsley, rosemary, walnuts, and salt and pepper to taste.

6 Spoon the mushroom mixture onto the warm polenta fingers. Garnish with a little chopped parsley and serve immediately.

PER SERVING: 7 g protein, 12 g total fat, 2 g saturated fat, 10 mg cholesterol, 27 g carbohydrates, 3 g fibre.

SALSA & SHRIMP TACOS

Expand your taco horizons by adding seafood to the mix, which is common in taco-loving Latin countries. Low in fat and high in taste, shrimp makes a great taco filling.

SWAP
Flavours

Halibut fillets can be substituted for the shrimp.

INGREDIENT INTEL
Avocado contains lots of **folate**, which is also present in jalapenos.

	8 taco shells, crisp or soft	
	2 limes, juiced	
1 tbsp	jalapeno pepper, minced	15 mL
	1 garlic clove, minced	
	Shredded lettuce	
	Plain low-fat yogurt	
	Handful cilantro, finely chopped	
1 ½ pounds	large uncooked shrimp, peeled	750 g
	1 avocado, chopped or sliced	
	Prepared salsa	
1 tsp	ground cumin	5 mL

416
calories per serving

1 Soak wooden skewers in water, and preheat barbecue to high; adjust to medium after about 15 minutes. Meanwhile, combine lime juice, cilantro, garlic, jalapeno pepper, cumin, and a little olive oil in a bowl. Add shrimp and toss to evenly coat.

2 When barbecue is hot, skewer shrimp and place on grill; cook about 4 minutes on each side or until shrimp are opaque.

3 Warm taco shells, then assemble. Fill each with a few shrimp and top with yogurt, salsa, lettuce, avocado, and more cilantro, if you wish.

PER SERVING: 36 g protein, 19 g total fat, 3 g saturated fat, 28 g carbohydrates, 297 mg cholesterol, 7 g fibre.

THE SKINNY ON LETTUCE

Romaine lettuce's dark green leaaves are a sign that it's the most nutritious. Next best? Green leaf, then butterhead, then red leaf, with iceberg in last place.

SWAP & DROP
FAST FOOD

SWAP THIS | FOR THAT

DOMINO'S PIZZA

Extravaganzza (pepperoni, ham, Italian sausage, beef, onions, mushrooms, green peppers, black olives, and extra cheese)

580 calories

28 g fat (13 g saturated)

1,540 mg sodium

Veggie (black olives, onions, mushrooms, green peppers, and tomatoes)

380 calories

14 g fat (5 g saturated)

860 mg sodium

BURGER KING

TenderGrill Chicken BLT Salad (grilled chicken, iceberg and romaine lettuce, tomatoes, cheese, bacon bits, with Caesar dressing)

500 calories

39 g fat (13 g saturated)

1,470 mg sodium

BK Veggie Burger (soy pattie with lettuce, tomatoes, ketchup, mustard) **and a side garden salad** (with low-calorie Italian dressing)

310 calories

8 g fat (3 g saturated)

1,340 mg sodium

SUBWAY

6-inch Tuna Sub (with olives and fresh veggies)

533 calories

28 g fat (5 g saturated)

666 mg sodium

6-inch Roast Beef Sub (with fresh vegetables, no cheese)

278 calories

4 g fat (1 g saturated)

699 mg sodium

TIM HORTONS

French Vanilla Cappucino (medium), BLT, and side of Chili

970 calories

45 g fat (19 g saturated)

2,390 mg sodium

Skim milk, BBQ Chicken Wrap Snacker, and Hearty Vegetable Soup

350 calories

5 g fat (1 g saturated)

1,685 mg sodium

SWAP & DROP
FAST FOOD

SWAP THIS

FOR THAT

McDONALD'S

Southwest Crispy Chicken Sandwich and large fries

1,140 calories

56 g fat (11 g saturated)

1,820 mg sodium

Pesto Grilled Chicken McMini Sandwich and small fries

500 calories

24 g fat (4 g saturated)

730 mg sodium

TACO BELL

Fiesta Taco Salad

850 calories

45 g fat (11 g saturated)

1,690 mg sodium

Fresco Chicken Soft Taco

170 calories

5 g fat (1.5 g saturated)

670 mg sodium

KFC

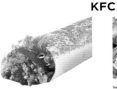

Crispy Chicken Strips Caesar Twister

650 calories

37 g fat (9 g saturated)

1,820 mg sodium

Tangy Caesar Salad with Grilled Chicken and Light Caesar Dressing (no croutons)

322 calories

9 g fat (5 g saturated)

1,117 mg sodium

WENDY'S

Baja Salad (greens, cheddar and pepperjack cheeses, chili, guacamole, pico de gallo, tortilla strips, and red jalapeno dressing)

740 calories

47.5 g fat (17.5 g saturated)

1,945 mg sodium

Apple Pecan Chicken Salad (greens, apple, pecans, blue cheese, dried cranberries, grilled chicken breast, and pomegranate vinaigrette dressing)

520 calories

26 g fat (9.5 g saturated)

1,350 mg sodium

ANOTHER SWAP
Try other breads, like whole-wheat English muffins, or seeded whole-wheat rolls.

GRILLED SALMON IN CIABATTA

SERVES 4

Here fresh salmon fillets are marinated, then lightly grilled and served in warm ciabatta rolls with mixed salad leaves and a basil mayonnaise, to create a tempting and special lunch dish. Using light mayonnaise and yogurt reduces the fat without losing any of the creaminess.

	Juice of 1 lime	
3 tbsp	fresh basil, chopped	45 mL
4 4-ounce	skinless salmon fillets	4 125-g
2 ½ tbsp	plain low-fat yogurt	35 mL
2 ½ tbsp	light mayonnaise	35 mL
½ tsp	finely grated lime zest	2 mL
	4 ciabatta or whole-wheat rolls	
	Salt and pepper, to taste	
	Mixed salad leaves, such as arugula, baby spinach, and red chard	

356 calories per serving

1 Mix lime juice, 2 tbsp (30 mL) of basil, and salt and pepper in a non-metallic dish. Add salmon and turn fillets in the mixture to coat well. Cover and marinate in the fridge for 30 minutes.

2 Meanwhile, mix together the yogurt, mayonnaise, lime zest, and remaining 1 tbsp (15 mL) basil in a small bowl. Season lightly with salt and pepper. Cover and refrigerate.

3 Heat broiler to medium-high. Remove salmon from the marinade and place on a foil-lined broiler rack. Brush with a little marinade, then grill until the fish is just cooked and flesh begins to flake, about 4 to 5 minutes per side, brushing again with marinade after turning. While the fish is cooking, place the ciabatta rolls, wrapped in foil, in the oven to warm for about 5 minutes.

4 Split the ciabatta rolls in half and spread the cut sides with the basil mayonnaise. Put a cooked salmon fillet on the bottom half of each roll and top with a few mixed salad leaves. Put the tops in place and serve immediately.

PER SERVING: 28 g protein, 13 g total fat, 2 g saturated fat, 78 mg cholesterol, 30 g carbohydrates, 2 g fibre.

1 MORE IDEA

● ● ● **Grilled Tuna Sandwiches with Tomato & Ginger Relish**

Use 4 (3-ounce/90-g) fresh tuna steaks, and marinate them in a mixture of 2 tsp (10 mL) finely chopped fresh rosemary, the juice of 1 orange, and salt and pepper to taste. To make the relish, sauté 1 finely chopped small red onion, 1 minced garlic clove, and 1 tbsp (15 mL) finely chopped fresh ginger in 2 tsp (10 mL) olive oil until softened, about 8 to 10 minutes. Remove from the heat and add 4 chopped plum tomatoes, 1-2 tbsp (15-30 mL) chopped fresh basil, and salt and pepper to taste. Mix well. Grill the tuna for 3 minutes on each side or until cooked to taste. Serve on whole-wheat rolls with lettuce leaves and the relish.

HUMMUS & TABOULEH SANDWICHES

SERVES 4

Savour the taste of this healthy Mediterranean-influenced recipe. You can find tahini (sesame paste) in health food and large grocery stores. Before adding the garlic to the hummus, press it with a knife into a paste. This helps it blend into the other ingredients.

371 calories per serving

1 19-ounce	can chickpeas, rinsed	1 540-mL
1 tbsp	tahini	15 mL
3 tbsp	water	45 mL
	2 cloves garlic, minced	
	2 pinches cumin	
3 tbsp	lemon juice, divided	45 mL
3 tbsp	extra virgin olive oil, divided	45 mL
	Salt and pepper, to taste	
1 cup	diced tomatoes	250 mL
1 cup	diced cucumbers	250 mL
1 cup	chopped parsley	250 mL
½ cup	coarsely chopped red onion	125 mL
¼ cup	chopped mint	60 mL
2 6 ½-inch	whole-wheat pitas, cut in half	2 16-cm

1 Make the hummus: Place chickpeas, tahini, water, garlic, cumin, and 2 tbsp (30 mL) each of lemon juice and olive oil in a food processor, and blend till smooth (or mash with a fork until smooth). Add salt and pepper to taste.

2 Make the tabouleh: In a medium bowl, toss together tomatoes, cucumbers, parsley, red onion, mint, and remaining olive oil and lemon juice. Adjust seasoning.

3 Spread one quarter of hummus in each pita half and fill with one quarter of the tabouleh.

PER SERVING: 11 g protein, 15 g total fat, 2 g saturated fat, 0 mg cholesterol, 52 g carbohydrates, 10 g fibre.

:) SESAME ALERT

While peanut allergies are better known, reactions to sesame seeds are among the fastest-growing allergies. They are still relatively rare, but if you notice a rash, swelling, or trouble breathing after eating the seeds (including tahini, a sauce form of sesame seeds), you may be allergic.

SPICY TURKEY QUESADILLAS

SERVES 2

A bit of spice livens up cranberries and turkey while fat-free cream cheese rounds out the flavours in this easy appetizer.

3 ounces	fat-free cream cheese	90 g
¼ cup	chopped fresh or frozen cranberries, thawed	60 mL
1 tbsp	chopped green chili peppers	15 mL
1 ½ tsp	honey	7 mL
1 tsp	Louisiana-style hot sauce	5 mL
4 6-inch	flour tortillas	4 15-cm
1 cup	diced cooked turkey breast	250 mL

343
calories per quesadilla

1 In a small bowl, beat cream cheese until smooth. Stir in the cranberries, green chili peppers, honey, and hot sauce until blended. Spread over one side of each tortilla. Place turkey on two tortillas; top with remaining tortillas.

2 Cook in a large non-stick frying pan over medium heat for 2 to 3 minutes on each side or until lightly browned. Cut quesadillas into wedges.

PER SERVING: 33 g protein, 7 g total fat, 1 g saturated fat, 64 mg cholesterol, 35 g carbohydrate, 1 g fibre.

Are you !#*@%?& kidding me?

Turkey breast is actually a little higher in protein than chicken breast. It's time to invite the big bird over more often!

MEDITERRANEAN HAMBURGERS
WITH RED-HOT TOMATO SALSA

SERVES 4

Sun-dried tomatoes, garlic, and herbs create a Mediterranean flavour, and a fresh chili-and-tomato salsa adds extra zip. Making your own burgers is so worthwhile, as they're much lower in fat than most prepared burgers, and you can flavour them as you please.

Advance planning

▶ Make the patties, cover with plastic wrap, and refrigerate for up to 2 days, or freeze for up to a month. Thaw before cooking. The salsa can be made the day before and stored in the refrigerator, covered with plastic wrap.

1 pound	lean ground beef	500 g
¼ cup	whole-grain breadcrumbs	60 mL
	2 garlic cloves, crushed	
¼ cup	sun-dried tomatoes in oil, drained and finely chopped	60 mL
2 tbsp	chopped fresh coriander	30 mL
	4 burger buns	
1 cup	Arugula lettuce	50 g
	TOMATO SALSA	
¼ pound	vine-ripened tomatoes, finely diced	250 g
	1 red pepper, deseeded and finely diced	
	½ mild green chili pepper, deseeded and finely chopped	
	1 red chili pepper, deseeded and finely chopped	
2 tsp	balsamic vinegar	10 mL
1 tbsp	snipped fresh chives	15 mL
1 tbsp	chopped fresh coriander	15 mL

428
calories per serving

1 Preheat a grill pan or turn on the broiler. Place the ground beef, breadcrumbs, garlic, sun-dried tomatoes, and coriander in a large bowl and use your hands to mix the ingredients together thoroughly.

2 Divide the mixture equally into four and shape into patties, about 4 inches (10 cm) across and a similar size to the buns.

3 Brush the grill rack or grill tray lightly with oil and cook the patties for 3 to 4 minutes on each side, until browned on the outside and cooked through.

4 To make the salsa, mix together all the ingredients in a bowl. (You can chop all the salsa ingredients together in the food processor to save time—just use the pulse button to get the right consistency.) Season to taste.

5 Split the buns in half and pop under the broiler or on the grill to toast lightly. Place a few arugula leaves on each base, top with a patty, and add a spoonful of salsa, then replace the tops. Serve immediately.

PER SERVING: 34 g protein, 12 g total fat, 4 g saturated fat, 51 mg cholesterol, 42 g carbohydrates, 5.5 g fibre.

FISH TACOS

Here's a truly fun way to enjoy fish. The mango's sweetness marries well with spicy peppers, creating a refreshing salsa.

380 calories per serving

1 tbsp	olive oil	15 mL
	2 cloves garlic, minced	
1 tsp	ground cumin	5 mL
3 tbsp	lime juice, divided	45 mL
1 ½ pounds	halibut fillets	700 g
	1 ripe mango, peeled, seeded, and chopped	
	½ small red pepper, seeded and finely chopped	
	½ jalapeno pepper, seeded, deveined, and finely chopped	
¼ cup	chopped cilantro (optional)	60 mL
	8 soft 6-inch (15-cm) corn tortillas	
1 cup	shredded lettuce	250 mL

INGREDIENT INTEL

Mangoes are deliciously rich in beta-carotene, vitamin C, potassium, and fibre and contain an enzyme with stomach-soothing properties. In this recipe, even the corn tortillas are rich in antioxidants.

1 Turn on the oven broiler. Coat a pan with cooking spray. In a medium bowl, combine oil, garlic, cumin, 1 tbsp (15 mL) lime juice, and the fish and toss to coat. Let stand 15 minutes.

2 In a small bowl, combine the mango, pepper, jalapeno, cilantro, if desired, and the remaining lime juice. Set aside.

3 Wrap the tortillas in foil. Remove the fish from the marinade and place on a broiler pan. Broil until opaque, 3 to 6 minutes. Transfer to a plate and place the tortillas in the oven to warm slightly, 1 minute. Flake the fish.

4 Top the tortillas with equal amounts of lettuce, fish, and salsa.

PER SERVING: 39 g protein, 9 g total fat, 1 g saturated fat, 54 mg cholesterol, 36 g carbohydrates, 5 g fibre.

LOW-SALT
Lower salt levels are easy to maintain when recipes like this can rely on bright flavours.

PIZZA POCKETS

Stuffed with a pizza-style filling, these special sandwiches surprise you with a burst of flavour in every bite.

183
calories per serving

	1 package active dry yeast	
1 cup	warm water (120-130°F/49-54°C)	250 mL
1 tbsp	sugar	15 mL
1 tbsp	butter, melted	15 mL
¼ tsp	salt	1 mL
3 to 3 ¼ cups	all-purpose flour	375 to 400 mL
1 8-ounce	can pizza sauce	225 g
	12 slices pepperoni	
1 2 ½-ounce	package thinly sliced fully cooked pastrami, chopped	70 g
1 2 ½-ounce	package thinly sliced fully cooked ham, chopped	70 g
¾ cup	shredded part-skim mozzarella cheese	180 mL
	1 egg, lightly beaten	

Size matters

◗ This is where portion control really works to give you a taste of your favourites without blowing the day's calories in a single meal. These pizza pockets seem decadent, but they're not when a slimming salad takes up half the plate, the pastrami and ham are lean, and the cheese is low-fat.

1 In a large mixing bowl, dissolve yeast in warm water. Add sugar, butter, salt, and 2 ¼ cups flour. Beat until smooth. Stir in enough remaining flour to form a soft dough.

2 Put onto a floured surface; knead for 6 to 8 minutes. Roll the dough into a 14 x 10-inch (35 x 25-cm) rectangle. Cut with a 3-inch (7.5-cm) round cookie cutter. Reroll scraps to cut a total of 24 circles. Place 1 tsp (5 mL) pizza sauce and slice of pepperoni in the centre of the 12 circles.

3 In a large bowl, combine the pastrami, ham, and cheese; place equal amounts over pepperoni. Top with ½ tsp (2 mL) of pizza sauce if desired. (Save remaining sauce for another use or use for dipping.) Cover with remaining dough circles; pinch edges or press with a fork to seal.

4 Place on greased baking sheets. Brush with egg. Bake at 400°F (200°C) for 20 to 25 minutes or until golden brown.

PER SERVINGS; 8 g protein, 5 g total fat, 2 g saturated fat, 33 mg cholesterol, 27 g carbohydrates, 1 g fibre.

THAI-STYLE BEEF SANDWICH

SERVES 4

There's enough of this spicy, refreshing slaw to serve on the side as well as on the sandwich.

2 tbsp	tomato paste	30 mL
½ cup	fresh lime juice (about 3 limes)	60 mL
1 ½ tsp	ground coriander	7 mL
1 pound	well-trimmed flank steak	450 g
1 tsp	sugar	5 mL
¼ tsp	salt	1 mL
1 tsp	red pepper flakes	5 mL
3 cups	packed shredded green cabbage	750 mL
	2 carrots, shredded	
	1 large red pepper, cut into matchsticks	
½ cup	chopped cilantro	125 mL
⅓ cup	chopped fresh mint	75 mL
	4 hard rolls, halved crosswise	

410 calories per serving

1 In a shallow non-aluminum pan, stir together the tomato paste, ¼ cup of the lime juice, and the ground coriander. Add the flank steak, turning it to coat. Refrigerate for 30 minutes.

2 In a large bowl, whisk together the remaining ½ cup lime juice, sugar, salt, and red pepper flakes. Add the cabbage, carrots, pepper, cilantro, and mint; toss well to combine. Refrigerate the slaw until serving time.

3 Preheat the broiler. Remove the steak from its marinade. Broil 6 inches (15 cm) from the heat for 4 minutes per side for medium-rare, brushing any remaining marinade over the steak. Let stand for 10 minutes before thinly slicing across the grain on the diagonal.

4 To serve, place the cabbage slaw on the bottom half of each cut roll. Top with ribbons of sliced steak.

PER SERVING: 31 g protein, 12 g total fat, 4 g saturated fat, 46 g carbohydrates, 57 mg cholesterol, 6 g fibre.

 DYNAMIC DUO

Enjoy a cup of green tea laced with lemon juice with this sandwich. A study of more than 40,000 Japanese adults found that those who enjoyed at least one cup of green tea daily were less likely to die of cardiovascualr disease than those who didn't. Another study showed that adding a splash of citrus juice to green tea helps the body absorb the tea's antioxidants.

SWAP & DROP

GOOD

331 *calories*

BETTER

253 *calories*

GRILLED VEGGIE & TURKEY BAGELS
SERVES 4

1 small zucchini, sliced lengthwise into 4 pieces

1 red pepper, seeded, cut in quarters

8 slices eggplant, thinly sliced

4 slices red onion

4 small portobello mushrooms

2 tbsp/30 mL extra virgin olive oil

Salt and pepper to taste

1 tbsp/15 mL balsamic vinegar

¼ cup/60 mL low-fat mayonnaise

1 tsp/5 mL fresh rosemary, finely chopped

2 multi-grain bagels, halved

¼ pound/200 g turkey breast, thinly sliced

1 In a medium bowl, place zucchini, red pepper, eggplant, red onion, mushrooms, and olive oil; toss until covered.

2 Turn on your oven broiler or heat grill pan to high. Place vegetables on grill pan (or a baking sheet, if using broiler), season with salt and pepper, and cook until they soften. Turn and grill until cooked through. Remove from heat, place back in bowl, and sprinkle with balsamic vinegar.

3 In a small bowl, mix together mayonnaise and rosemary. Toast each bagel half. Spread mayo mixture on each, then top with turkey and vegetables.

PER SERVING: 19 g protein, 14 g total fat, 3 g saturated fat, 39 mg cholesterol, 34 g carbohydrates, 8 g fibre.

CURRIED CHICKEN SALAD SANDWICHES
SERVES 4

¼ cup/60 mL low-fat plain yogurt

2 tbsp/30 mL low-fat canola mayonnaise

1 ½ tsp/7 mL curry powder

1 tsp/5 mL honey

¼ tsp/1 mL salt

2 cups/500 mL chopped cooked chicken

1 apple, cored and chopped

2 celery stalks, chopped

4 lettuce leaves

2 8-inch (30-cm) whole-grain pita breads, halved

1 In a large bowl, whisk together the yogurt, mayonnaise, curry powder, honey, and salt. Add the chicken, apple, and celery.

2 Place a lettuce leaf in each pita half and fill with ¼ of the chicken salad.

PER SERVING: 23 g protein, 6 g total fat, 1 g saturated fat, 53 mg cholesterol, 27 g carbohydrates, 4 g fibre.

TUNA & CARROT SANDWICH ON RYE

SERVES 2

Adding more omega-3–rich foods to your diet can be as simple as packing a tuna sandwich for lunch. This one is boosted by a lemony grated carrot salad, adding crunch and appeal while boosting your vegetable count. We've put it on rye bread, which can actually help lower your blood sugar.

	1 medium carrot, shredded	
2 tsp	lemon juice	10 mL
2 tsp	extra-virgin olive oil	10 mL
1 tbsp	chopped green onions	15 mL
1 tbsp	chopped fresh dill or parsley	15 mL
	Salt, to taste	
½ 6-ounce can	water-packed chunk light tuna, drained and flaked	½ 184-g can
¼ cup	finely chopped celery	60 mL
2 tbsp	reduced-fat mayonnaise, divided	30 mL
	4 slices rye or pumpernickel bread	
	4 lettuce leaves, rinsed and dried	

303 calories per serving

1 Combine the carrot, lemon juice, oil, green onion, dill (or parsley), and salt in a small bowl. Toss with a fork to mix.

2 Mix the tuna, celery, and 1 tbsp (15 mL) of the mayonnaise in a small bowl. Spread the remaining 1 tbsp (15 mL) mayonnaise over the bread slices. Spread half of the tuna mixture over two of the bread slices. Top with the carrot salad and lettuce. Set remaining bread slices over filling. Cut each sandwich in half.

PER SERVING: 17 g protein, 9 g total fat, 2 g saturated fat, 13 mg cholesterol, 38 g carbohydrates, 5 g fibre.

LUNCHBOX TIP

The sandwiches will keep, well wrapped, in the refrigerator or a cooler packed with ice packs for up to 1 day.

These light meals fit the bill when you seek something a little more substantial. Many are perfect for a luncheon when having friends over for a leisurely midday meal.

MEDITERRANEAN STUFFED PEPPERS

SERVES 4

These pretty peppers are a gorgeous way to serve up more veggies.

2 tsp	olive oil	10 mL
1 tsp	each ground cumin and coriander	5 mL
	1 small onion, chopped	
	1 small handful fresh mint, chopped	
½ cup	crumbled feta	125 mL
¾ cup	dry whole-wheat couscous	175 mL
5 ounce	bag of baby spinach	142 g
⅔ pound	ground turkey	300 g
	4 large peppers, any colour, cut in halves	

366 calories per serving

1 Preheat oven to 400°F (200°C). Place the pepper halves with cut side down in a large casserole or baking sheet. Bake for 10 minutes.

2 Meanwhile, cook couscous according to package directions, and set aside.

3 Pour olive oil into a large frying pan over medium heat, add onion and sauté until soft, 5 minutes. Increase heat to medium-high; add cumin, coriander, chili flakes (if using), and turkey—cook until browned and cooked through, about 3 minutes.

4 Toss in spinach; stir until wilted, about 2 minutes. Mix in the couscous, mint and feta.

5 Spoon this mixture into the pepper halves. Bake, filled side up, until filling is heated through, about 8 to 10 minutes. Put 2 pepper halves on each of 4 plates, mixing or matching the colours.

PER SERVING 23 g protein, 13 g total fat, 5 g saturated fat, 76 mg cholesterol, 39 g carbohydrates, 6 g fibre.

CHICKEN JAMBOREE

This one-pan casserole makes an easy mid-week meal. Serve with brown rice.

	Cooking spray	
12 ounces	skinless, boneless chicken breasts, diced	375 g
	1 small onion, chopped	
8 ounces	mushrooms	250 g
	1 bay leaf	
½ tsp	2 large sprigs fresh or dried thyme	2 mL
½ tsp	3 large sprigs fresh tarragon or dried tarragon (optional)	2 mL
	Zest of 1 small lemon	
½ cup	dry sherry	125 mL
1 ¼ cups	boiling water	300 mL
1 cup	baby carrots	250 mL
1 cup	broccoli florets	250 mL
1 tbsp	flour	15 mL
3 tbsp	fresh parsley, chopped	45 mL
	Salt and pepper, to taste	

170 calories per serving

1 Heat a large non-stick frying pan, coated with cooking spray, over medium-high heat. Add chicken and cook for 3 minutes, stirring constantly. Reduce heat to medium and stir in onion, mushrooms, bay leaf, thyme, tarragon, and lemon zest. Cook until vegetables begin to soften.

2 Add sherry, water, carrots, salt, and pepper, and stir well. Bring to a boil, then reduce the heat to low and cover the pan. Simmer for 5 minutes. Add broccoli florets and bring the liquid back to a simmer. Cover and cook until the chicken is tender and the vegetables are cooked, about 5 minutes. Remove and discard the bay leaf, thyme, and tarragon, if using fresh herbs.

3 Blend flour and 2 tbsp (30 mL) cold water to form a paste. Stir flour mixture into the frying pan and simmer, stirring constantly, until thickened, about 2 minutes. Sprinkle with parsley.

PER SERVING: 22 g protein, 3 g total fat, 1 g saturated fat, 51 mg cholesterol, 12 g carbohydrates, 2 g fibre.

POTATO & ZUCCHINI TORTILLA

SERVES 6

This Spanish-style tortilla is made from the simplest of ingredients and served warm or cold, cut into wedges. Serve with a fresh tomato salsa, salad, and bread.

1 ½ pounds	new potatoes, peeled and cut into ½-inch (1-cm) cubes	750 g
2 tbsp	olive oil	30 mL
	1 red onion, finely chopped	
	1 zucchini, diced	
	2 slices turkey bacon, chopped	
	6 eggs	
2 tbsp	chopped parsley	30 mL
	Pepper	
½ tsp	red pepper flakes (optional)	2 mL

161 calories per serving

1 Simmer potato cubes for 3 minutes. Drain thoroughly. Heat the oil in a heavy (10-inch/25-cm) non-stick frying pan. Add the potatoes, onion, zucchini, and bacon, and cook over medium heat until the potatoes are tender and lightly golden, about 10 minutes, turning from time to time.

2 Heat the broiler to high. In a bowl, beat eggs with 1 tbsp (15 mL) cold water. Add parsley and pepper to taste. Pour egg mixture over vegetables in the frying pan and cook until egg has set on the base (3-4 minutes), lifting the edges to allow uncooked egg mixture to run onto the pan.

3 When there is just a little uncooked egg on the top, place the pan under the broiler and cook for 2 minutes to set the top. Slide the tortilla out onto a plate or board and let cool for 2 to 3 minutes. Cut into wedges and serve warm, or let to cool completely before cutting and serving.

PER SERVING: 7 g protein, 8 g total fat, 2 g saturated fat, 162 mg cholesterol, 16 g carbohydrates, 2 g fibre.

SWAP IT OUT!

● ● ● **Potato & Asparagus Tortilla**

Instead of zucchini, try chopped asparagus, or add chopped tomatoes or cooked peas just before pouring in the eggs. Fresh tarragon, chives, or basil can be used in place of parsley.

LOWER FAT
Three cups of egg substitute can be used in place of the whole eggs to decrease the fat and cholesterol content.

FRESH IDEA
Steeping chopped rosemary leaves in olive oil and using it for dipping slender slices of a baguette is a fresh-tasting partner for this summery dish.

TOMATO & ROMANO CHEESE BAKE

SERVES 4

For this attractive dish, sweet cherry tomatoes are baked in a light, fluffy batter and sprinkled with grated Romano cheese. Many egg dishes are made with whole eggs and cream. Here, the batter is made with a combination of whole eggs, egg whites, and light sour cream to make a delightful lower-fat version. Make individual servings in small ramekins or one large one and serve for a simple lunch or supper. Boiled new potatoes and fresh green beans are excellent accompaniments.

	Cooking spray	
1 pound	cherry tomatoes	500 g
4 tbsp	snipped fresh chives	60 mL
⅓ cup	coarsely grated Romano cheese	75 mL
	3 large eggs	
	3 egg whites	
2 tbsp	flour	30 mL
3 tbsp	light sour cream	45 mL
1 ¼ cups	1% milk	300 mL
	Pepper	

185 calories per serving

1 Preheat the oven to 375°F (190°C). Lightly spray 4 shallow ovenproof dishes, each about 5 to 6 inches (12 to 15 cm) in diameter. Divide the cherry tomatoes among the dishes, spreading them out, and sprinkle over top the chives and 4 tbsp (60 mL) of the cheese.

2 Break the eggs into a bowl and whisk them together with the egg whites, then gradually whisk in the flour until smooth. Add the sour cream, then gradually whisk in the milk to make a thin, smooth batter. Season lightly with pepper.

3 Pour the batter over the tomatoes, dividing it evenly among the dishes. Sprinkle over the remaining cheese and an extra grinding of pepper. Bake until set, puffed, and lightly golden, about 30 to 35 minutes.

4 Remove the dishes from the oven and leave to cool for a few minutes before serving, as the tomatoes will be very hot inside.

PER SERVING: 15 g protein, 8 g total fat, 3 g saturated fat, 150 mg cholesterol, 14 g carbohydrates, 2 g fibre.

SWAP
down cholesterol

TWO EGG WHITES CAN BE used in place of one whole egg in almost all recipes. This eliminates the yolk of the egg, which contains about 215 mg cholesterol. The substitution is particularly useful in recipes for baked goods, such as cakes and quick breads.

PEARS BROILED WITH PECORINO

Tuscany brings us this traditional pairing of sweet pears with savoury pecorino.

6 cups	arugula, leaves removed from stems	1.5 L
2 cups	watercress (1 bunch), stems removed	500 mL
1 cup	seedless green grapes, halved	250 mL
3 ounces	pecorino (or Romano) cheese	90 g
	2 large, ripe pears, such as Comice or Bartlett	
	VINAIGRETTE	
¼ cup	olive oil	60 mL
3 tbsp	balsamic vinegar	45 mL
1 tsp	Dijon mustard	5 mL
½ tsp	sugar	2 mL
¼ tsp	salt	1 mL
¼ tsp	freshly ground black pepper	1 mL

317 calories per serving

1 First, make the dressing. Place the oil, vinegar, mustard, sugar, salt, and pepper into a 2-cup (500-mL) jar or container with a tight-fitting lid. Cover and shake until well blended. Chill.

2 In a large salad bowl, toss the arugula, watercress, and green grapes. Using a vegetable peeler or cheese slicer, cut the pecorino into thin slices. Roughly chop half and toss into the salad bowl. Set aside the rest of the slices for melting on the pears.

3 Heat the broiler to high and line a baking sheet with foil. Peel the pears, cut them in half and core them. Arrange, cut sides down, on the baking sheet. Top with reserved cheese, overlapping the slices. Broil the pears, 6 inches (15 cm) from the heat source just until the cheese begins to bubble, about 2 minutes.

4 Drizzle dressing it over the salad and toss until coated. Mound the salad equally on 4 plates. Using a small spatula, carefully arrange one pear half on each. Serve at once while the cheese is warm and the greens are crisp.

PER SERVING: 9 g protein, 21 g total fat, 6 g saturated fat, 23 mg cholesterol, 28 g carbohydrates, 4 g fibre.

SWAP IT OUT!

● ● ● Nectarines Grilled with Gorgonzola

Substitute 3 ounces (90 g) Gorgonzola cheese for the pecorino. Using a serrated knife, slice the cheese as thin as possible. Toss half into the salad. Place the nectarines on the baking sheet cut-side up and stuff the cavities with the remaining cheese. Broil the nectarines just until the cheese melts.

● ● ● Raspberries with Grilled Brie

Make the dressing with 3 tbsp (45 mL) raspberry vinegar instead of balsamic. Make the salad, substituting 1 cup (250 mL) ripe raspberries for the grapes and 3 ounces (90 g) brie cheese for the pecorino. Stuff the cavities of the pears with the brie and broil cut side up.

BOLOGNESE BEEF POT

SERVES 4

Lemon and fennel bring wonderfully fresh flavours to familiar braised ground beef in this Italian-inspired dish, as good for alfresco dining as it is for a light winter supper.

334 calories per serving

¾ pound	extra-lean ground beef	375 g
	1 onion, chopped	
	2 garlic cloves, minced	
1 pound	potatoes, scrubbed and finely diced	500 g
28 ounces	chopped tomatoes (1 large can)	796 mL
¾ cup	low-sodium chicken broth	175 mL
	Zest and juice of 1 lemon	
½ tsp	brown sugar	2 mL
	Pepper	
	1 fennel bulb, thinly sliced (reserve the leaves)	
1 cup	frozen green beans	250 mL
	GARNISH	
	Chopped fennel leaves, chopped fresh flat-leaf parsley	

1 Place ground beef, onion, and garlic in a large saucepan and cook over medium heat, stirring frequently until the meat is evenly browned. Stir in potatoes, tomatoes with their juice, broth, half the lemon zest, sugar, and pepper. Bring to a boil, then reduce the heat to low and simmer for 10 minutes, stirring once or twice to ensure that the potatoes cook evenly.

2 Stir in fennel, frozen beans, and lemon juice. Cover and simmer until the potatoes are tender and the fennel and beans are lightly cooked but still crisp, about 5 minutes. Spoon the mixture into serving bowls. Garnish with remaining lemon zest, fennel leaves, and parsley.

PER SERVING: 25 g protein, 8 g total fat, 3 g saturated fat, 57 mg cholesterol, 43 g carbohydrates, 8 g fibre.

Great go-with

▶ A green salad tossed with thinly sliced red onion, a handful of fresh basil, a few black olives, and a lemon—olive oil dressing tastes excellent with this dish, providing contrasting texture as well as flavour.

SWAP & DROP

GOOD

224 *calories*

SMOKED HADDOCK & POTATO PIE

SERVES 6

2 ¼ cups plus 3 tbsp/550 mL plus 45 mL skim milk

1 pound/500 g smoked haddock fillets

1 bay leaf

1 large leek, halved and sliced

1 lb/500 g russet potatoes, cut in ¼ inch (0.5 cm) slices

3 tbsp/45 mL cornmeal

2 cups/500 mL watercress

½ cup/125 mL grated low-fat cheddar cheese

Pepper

Chopped parsley

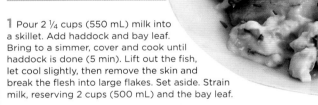

1 Pour 2 ¼ cups (550 mL) milk into a skillet. Add haddock and bay leaf. Bring to a simmer, cover and cook until haddock is done (5 min). Lift out the fish, let cool slightly, then remove the skin and break the flesh into large flakes. Set aside. Strain milk, reserving 2 cups (500 mL) and the bay leaf.

2 Place leek in the frying pan; add reserved milk and bay leaf. Cover and simmer until leek is tender (10 minutes). Meanwhile, boil potatoes until just tender (8 minutes); drain. Preheat oven to 375°F (190°C).

3 Discard the bay leaf. Mix cornmeal with 3 tbsp (45 mL) cold milk. Add to the leek mixture and cook gently, stirring, until slightly thickened. Off the heat, stir in the watercress, let wilt. Season with pepper. Fold the haddock in gently into a 9-inch (23-cm) pie plate.

4 Transfer to a pie plate, overlapping potato slices on top. Sprinkle with cheese and season with pepper. Bake until the fish filling is bubbling and the potatoes turn golden, 25 to 30 minutes. Sprinkle with parsley and let stand 5 minutes before serving.

PER SERVING: 26 g protein, 3 g total fat, 1 g saturated fat, 67 mg cholesterol, 23 g carbohydrates, 2 g fibre.

BETTER

160 *calories*

SMOKED HADDOCK SOUFFLÉ

SERVES 6

⅔ pound/300 g smoked haddock fillet

1 ¼ cups/300 mL 1% milk

1 tsp/ 5 mL butter

1 tbsp/15 mL grated Parmesan

1 tbsp/15 mL dry breadcrumbs

3 tbsp/45 mL flour

3 eggs, separated

2 tomatoes, peeled, seeded, and diced

1 tsp/5 mL grainy mustard

2 tbsp/30 mL finely chopped parsley

2 tbsp/30 mL snipped chives

1 egg white

Pepper

1 Place the haddock and milk in a saucepan, heat and simmer until done (8 minutes). Let cool, then remove and flake the flesh, discarding skin and bones. Let milk cool.

2 Preheat a metal baking sheet to 375°F (190°C). Lightly grease a 6-cup (1.5-L) soufflé dish with butter. Mix Parmesan and breadcrumbs, sprinkle in dish, then shake out and reserve excess.

3 Mix flour with a little cold poaching milk. Heat remaining milk then pour into the flour mixture, stirring constantly. Return to the pan and bring to a boil, stirring to make a thick sauce. Pour into a large bowl, beat in egg yolks one by one. Stir in the flaked haddock, tomatoes, mustard, parsley, and chives. Add pepper to taste.

4 In a clean mixing bowl, whisk 4 egg whites to soft peaks. Gently fold ¼ of the whites, then the rest, into the mixture. Spoon into the soufflé dish; sprinkle with reserved crumbs. Bake on the hot sheet until well puffed and golden brown, about 35 minutes. Serve at once.

PER SERVING: 20 g protein, 5 g total fat, 2 g saturated fat, 150 mg cholesterol, 9 g carbohydrates, 1 g fibre.

CHICKEN & CASHEW CRÊPES

SERVES 4

This makes a delicious filling for thin pancakes you can make or buy. If time is short, try it tucked into in a multigrain wrap.

Cashews, like all nuts, are important for heart health. It might be due to their monounsaturated fat, vitamin E, fibre, minerals, or antioxidants. What a powerhouse!

Crêpes (see recipe page 228)		
⅓ cup	cashews	50 g
1 tbsp	sunflower oil	15 mL
⅔ pound	chicken breasts, cut into strips	300 g
	1 garlic clove, minced	
1 tsp	finely chopped fresh ginger	5 mL
	1 small red chili pepper, seeded and finely chopped	
	2 carrots, cut into matchsticks	
	2 celery stalks, cut into matchsticks	
	Grated rind of ½ orange	
	½ Savoy or Chinese cabbage, shredded	
1 tbsp	reduced-salt soy sauce, plus extra to serve	15 mL
1 tsp	sesame oil	5 mL

455 calories per serving

1 To make the filling, heat a wok or large frying pan. Add the cashews and dry-fry over medium heat for a few minutes or until golden. Remove and set aside. Add the oil to the wok and swirl it around, then add the chicken, garlic, ginger, and chili pepper. Stir-fry for 3 minutes.

2 Add the carrot and celery sticks, and stir-fry for a further 2 minutes. Add the orange rind and cabbage and stir-fry for 1 minute. Sprinkle over the soy sauce and sesame oil and stir-fry for another minute. Return the cashews to the pan and toss to mix with the other ingredients.

3 Divide the filling among the warm crêpes and fold them over or roll up. Serve immediately, with a little extra soy sauce to sprinkle.

PER SERVING: 32 g protein, 20 g total fat, 4 g saturated fat, 118 mg cholesterol, 36 g carbohydrates, 5 g fibre.

CHICKEN & VEGETABLE PHYLLO ROLLS

SERVES 8

Serve on a bed of salad greens topped with a colourful cranberry mustard.

156 calories per serving

SWAP IT OUT!

⬤ ⬤ ⬤ **Greek Spinach & Chicken Phyllo Pockets**

Substitute 2 cups (500 mL) slivered fresh spinach leaves for the cabbage. Omit the ham, bread crumbs, and sage. To the vegetables add the chicken, onion, thyme, pepper, and salt, plus 1 cup (250 mL) cooked white rice and 3 tbsp (45 mL) fresh lemon juice. Cut the 8 phyllo sheets into 16 (6 inch/15 cm) squares.

For each phyllo parcel, spray with butter-flavoured cooking spray, cover with a second square and spray again. Place ⅛ of the filling in a triangular shape, slightly off-centre, near one corner. Fold the pastry over the filling to make a triangular parcel, matching up the opposite corner and sealing the sides. Sprinkle with 2 tsp (10 mL) poppy seeds instead of the sesame seeds. Bake for 30 minutes and serve on a bed of salad leaves. Omit the cranberry mustard. Finish cooking the remaining batter.

	2 large carrots, peeled and cut into julienne strips	
2 cups	Savoy cabbage with curly dark green leaves, shredded	500 mL
	3 slivered green onions	
½ pound	ground uncooked chicken breast	250 g
1 cup	lean cooked smoked ham, minced	250 mL
1 cup	finely chopped yellow onion	250 mL
2 tbsp	dry plain bread crumbs	30 mL
2 tbsp	chopped fresh sage leaves	30 mL
2 tsp	chopped fresh thyme leaves	10 mL
1 tsp	freshly ground black pepper	5 mL
¼ tsp	salt	1 mL
	8 18 x 14-inch (45 x 35 cm) sheets phyllo pastry	
	Butter-flavoured cooking spray	
2 tsp	sesame seeds	10 mL
2 cups	mesclun salad greens	500 mL
	CRANBERRY MUSTARD	
1 cup	canned jellied cranberry sauce	250 mL
2 tbsp	red wine vinegar	30 mL
1 tbsp	olive oil	15 mL
1 tsp	Dijon mustard	5 mL

1 First, make the filling. Bring half a medium saucepan of water to a boil over high heat. Add carrots, cabbage, and green onions, then blanch for 1 minute. Transfer to a colander and rinse with cold running water. Pat the vegetables dry and place in a large bowl. Mix in the chicken, ham, yellow onion, bread crumbs, sage, thyme, pepper, and salt; set aside.

2 Preheat the oven to 375°F (190°C) and set out a nonstick baking sheet. Cut the 8 phyllo sheets in half lengthwise, making 16 pieces. Trim each into a thin strip, 15 x 6 inches (38 x 15 cm), and cover quickly with plastic wrap, then a damp towel. Phyllo dries quickly, so work fast!

3 For each roll, use 2 strips. Spray one strip lightly with butter-flavoured spray, then top with the second. Spray again. Place ⅛ of the filling across one end. Roll up, folding in the long sides as you go for a parcel about 5 inches (13 cm) long and 2 inches (5 cm) in diameter. Place the parcel on a baking sheet, seam side down, and spray again. Repeat with the rest. Using a serrated knife, make 3 shallow slashes across the top of each parcel. Spray again. Sprinkle with sesame seeds. Bake until golden, about 30 minutes.

4 Meanwhile, shake cranberry mustard ingredients in a screw-top jar until blended. Edge each plate with a 1 tbsp (15 mL) of cranberry mustard, place a phyllo roll on a mound of salad greens.

PER SERVING: 13 g protein, 4 g total fat, 1 g saturated fat, 28 mg cholesterol, 18 g carbohydrates, 2 g fibre.

Salty snacks

Try these smarter picks when you're jonesing for some salt.

1. Cheesy kale chips: Tear kale leaves into large pieces and arrange on a baking sheet. Spritz with olive oil and bake at 350°F/175°C until crisp. Sprinkle with Parmesan.
2. A few tamari-seasoned rice crackers are great to scoop tuna salad. Punch it up with a squeeze of chili sauce!
3. Drain canned artichoke hearts and sprinkle with lemon zest, capers, chopped fresh basil and olive oil.
4. Five-spice pumpkin seeds: Toss salted seeds with sesame oil and Chinese five-spice powder; bake at 350°F/175°C until crisp.
5. Whole-wheat pretzels are flat-out irresistible when slathered with spicy mustard (which has few calories).

4 DEADLY CRAVINGS

SNACK SMARTER

Salty, crunchy, sweet, creamy: For every nasty craving that attacks between meals, we've come up with 5 healthier options

Don't even think about nachos; these snacks offer the same satisfying crunch.

Buffalo popcorn
Toss air-popped popcorn with olive oil, a little hot sauce or chili powder, and a sprinkle of Parmesan cheese.

Easy salsa
Chop up tomatoes, cucumber, peppers, and onions in a mini chopper, and put it on Melba toast.

Crunchy snacks

Swap potato chips for one of these.

1. Dunk root veggie chips (such as Terra chips) into low-fat plain yogurt seasoned with hot sauce and orange zest.
2. Chickpea poppers: Drain and rinse canned chickpeas; dry with a paper towel. Spritz with extra virgin olive oil, season with oregano and garlic salt; roast at 400°F/200°C until crisp.
3. Dip sugar snap peas into warm goat cheese (30 seconds in the microwave should do it).
4. Fill endive spears with chopped pears and season with a dash of balsamic vinegar.
5. Combine finely chopped broccoli, multicoloured peppers, and green onions with Greek yogurt and onion flakes. Use it as a dip for baby carrots. Crunch!

Creamy snacks

For those days when you just want a whipped-cream-drenched treat, a bowl of ice cream, or a velvety dip, these healthy snacks taste rich and smooth.

1 Microwave a small sweet potato, split it open, and mash a little orange juice into it. Eat it right out of the jacket.

2 Spread baba ghanouj, crushed avocado, or hummus on a whole-wheat pita or an English muffin.

3 Baby red potatoes become blissfully soft when you microwave them for 3 to 5 minutes (leave the skin on for nutrients). Sprinkle with pepper and dried seasonings, and pop them in your mouth.

4 Treat yourself to the most sublimely simple protein-packed treat: a soft-scrambled egg.

5 Raid the supermarket antipasto bar for some lusciously creamy slow-roasted red peppers. Pat the oil off with a paper towel and eat with a mini bocconcini or two. *Delicioso!*

Mash canned white beans with olive oil and some chopped fresh rosemary. Pile onto radicchio or lettuce leaves.

If you seek a fast sugar fix, indulge in a few dates—one of nature's sweetest treats.

Fruit skewers Spear the sweetest fruits—strawberries, mango, grapes and pineapple—with bamboo skewers.

Sweet snacks

We're hard-wired to love sugar—but you can indulge without reaching for a candy bar, donut, or chocolate cake. These good-for-you snacks take advantage of the sweetness found in whole foods.

1 Fold chopped ripe nectarines into low-fat cottage cheese and spoon onto a couple of gingersnaps.

2 Minimalist, yet amazingly delicious: sprinkle cocoa nibs (small chunks of cocoa beans) on canned pears.

3 Stir a little maple syrup into Greek yogurt and dip in slices of apples or pears.

4 When it feels like banana cream pie would really hit the spot, try this. Grab some graham crackers, spread them with vanilla Greek yogurt, and top with a handful of banana slices and a sprinkle of ground flaxseed.

5 Transform a simple grapefruit into something more like crème brûlée; halve it, drizzle with dark honey, and broil until bubbly.

COUNT 'EM
Dont forget to count between-meal snacks: those who do count all calories have the best dieting results, according to a review of 80 weight-loss trials.

Appetizers

Appetizers are the adorable babies of any menu: delightful nuggets, rounds, dabs, and packets, these cuties perk up your palate while taking the edge off your appetite. Combine a few of these flavourful finger foods for a tapas-style supper, served with plenty of fresh greens dressed in a simple vinaigrette.

CHICKEN YAKITORI

MAKES 30

These delicious Japanese-style bites of chicken speared with green pepper and green onions can be assembled in advance and then grilled just before serving. For the best flavour, leave the chicken to marinate for several hours or overnight, and remember to soak the skewers first so they do not burn.

3 tbsp	light soy sauce	45 mL
3 tbsp	sake or dry sherry	45 mL
1 tbsp	toasted sesame oil	15 mL
	1 garlic clove, minced	
1 tbsp	finely chopped fresh ginger	15 mL
2 tsp	honey	10 mL
1 pound	skinless, boneless chicken breasts, cut into 1-inch (2.5-cm) cubes	500 g
	1 large green pepper, seeded and cut into small cubes	
	6 large green onions, cut across into 30 pieces	

56 calories per 2 skewers

1 Place the soy sauce, sake, sesame oil, garlic, ginger, and honey in a shallow dish and stir together to mix. Add the chicken pieces and spoon the marinade over them. Cover and marinate in the refrigerator for at least 1 hour or overnight.

2 Just before cooking, put 30 short wooden skewers in warm water and leave to soak for 10 minutes. Turn on oven broiler or preheat a grill pan.

3 Thread 2 pieces of chicken onto each skewer, alternating with a piece of pepper and one of green onion, threaded widthwise. Place the kebabs on the grill pan or under the broiler and cook until tender (about 10 to 15 minutes), turning from time to time and brushing with the marinade. Serve hot.

PER SERVING: 7 g protein, 2 g total fat, 0 g saturated fat, 18 mg cholesterol, 3 g carbohydrates, 0 g fibre.

ROSEMARY MARINATED OLIVES

The flavour of olives is greatly enhanced by marinating them in fruity olive oil with fresh herbs and citrus juices. When mixed with bright veggies, they look and taste fabulous. For best flavour, allow about 2 days of marinating.

1 ½ cups	pitted olives, preferably a mixture of black and green	375 mL
2 tbsp	olive oil (preferably extra virgin)	30 mL
1 tbsp	lemon juice	15 mL
	1 thin-skinned orange, scrubbed but unpeeled, cut in small chunks	
	2 sprigs of fresh rosemary	
	1 fresh green chili pepper, seeded and thinly sliced	
	1 red pepper, seeded and cut in small chunks	
	1 yellow pepper, seeded and cut in small chunks	
½ cup	halved cherry tomatoes	125 mL

81 calories per serving

1 Place the olives in a large bowl and add the olive oil, lemon juice, chunks of orange, rosemary sprigs, and chili pepper. Stir together, then cover. Refrigerate.

2 For the next 2 days, every 12 hours or so, take the olive mixture from the fridge, uncover, and stir. Cover again and return to the fridge.

3 When ready to eat, combine the marinated olives with the red and yellow peppers and tomatoes, and stir well. Divide into 8 servings.

PER SERVING: 1 g protein, 4 g total fat, 6 g saturated fat, 0 mg cholesterol, 7 g carbohydrates, 2 g fibre.

TASTY TIP
Olives are highly valued for their mainly monounsaturated oil content; green ones have more vitamin A than black. Add the marinated olives to salads. They go well with fresh spinach and chickpeas, or tuna and cucumber.

CHERRY TOMATOES WITH PESTO CREAM CHEESE SERVES 16

Pesto and tomatoes are a time-honoured combination. In this recipe, pesto is thickened with low-fat cream cheese to make a filling that bursts with the flavour of summer and makes an exceptionally attractive appetizer. You can make the filling ahead of time (refrigerate covered up to 2 days), but stuff just before serving.

3 cups	fresh basil leaves, washed and dried	750 mL
⅓ cup	plus 2 tbsp toasted pine nuts, divided	60 g
	2 medium garlic cloves, minced	
½ tsp	salt, or to taste	2 mL
	Freshly ground pepper to taste	
1 tbsp	extra-virgin olive oil	15 mL
8 ounces	Neufchâtel cream cheese, cut in chunks	250 g
4 cups	cherry tomatoes	1 L

70 calories per 3 tomatoes

1 Combine the basil, ⅓ cup pine nuts, garlic, salt, and pepper in a food processor. Process until pine nuts are ground. With motor running, drizzle in olive oil. Add cream cheese and pulse until smooth and creamy.

2 Shortly before serving, cut an X on the rounded side (opposite the stem) of each cherry tomato with a serrated or sharp paring knife. Scoop out the seeds with a grapefruit spoon or your fingertips, taking care to keep the tomatoes intact.

3 Scrape the cream cheese filling into a pastry bag fitted with a star tip or small plastic food bag with a ½-inch (1-cm) hole snipped in one corner. Pipe a rosette of filling into each cherry tomato cavity. Garnish the cherry tomatoes with the remaining pine nuts.

PER SERVING: 2 g protein, 6 g total fat, 2 g saturated fat, 8 mg cholesterol, 2 g carbohydrates, 0 g fibre.

HOW TO TOAST PINE NUTS

Toast pine nuts in a small dry frying pan over medium-low heat, stirring constantly, until light golden and fragrant, which takes 2 to 3 minutes. Transfer to a small bowl to let cool.

SIMPLE SWAP Neufchâtel is cream cheese that is made with about one-third less fat and is slightly moister than regular cream cheese.

GINGERED CRAB PHYLLO DUMPLINGS

MAKES 18

These Asian-style triangular dumplings made of crisp, light phyllo pastry envelop a ginger-flavoured filling of crab, water chestnuts and corn. They look and taste wonderful, and are surprisingly simple to make. Prepare them ahead for a party, then bake just before serving with a sweet chili dipping sauce.

7 ounces	white crabmeat (1 can)	200 g
½ cup	canned water chestnuts, drained and coarsely chopped	125 mL
1 ½ cups	frozen corn, thawed	375 mL
	4 green onions, chopped	
1 tbsp	finely chopped fresh ginger	15 mL
	1 fresh red chili pepper, seeded, deveined, finely chopped	
2 tbsp	Chinese cooking wine (mirin) or dry sherry	30 mL
2 tbsp	canola oil	30 mL
1 tbsp	toasted sesame oil	15 mL
	6 sheets phyllo pastry	
1 tbsp	sesame seeds	15 mL
	Salt and pepper	
	GARNISH	
	Thai sweet chili dipping sauce	
	Green onions	

63 calories per dumpling

1 Preheat the oven to 400°F (200°C). Combine the crabmeat, water chestnuts, corn, green onions, ginger, red chili pepper (wear gloves; they burn), and wine in a bowl, and season lightly with salt and pepper. Mix the canola and sesame oils in a cup.

2 Roll up each of the 6 sheets of phyllo pastry loosely, rolling from a short side. Using a sharp knife, cut each roll across evenly into 3 pieces. Cover these shorter rolls with plastic wrap to prevent them from drying out. To make the dumplings, open the rolls one at a time and keep the rest aside, covered.

3 Lay a strip of phyllo flat, with a short end nearest to you, and brush with a little of the oil mixture. Place a heaping teaspoon (5 mL) of the crab mixture near the bottom, toward the right-hand corner of the short end, and fold the pastry diagonally over it. Continue folding diagonally, over and over, until you reach the end of the strip, making a neat triangular parcel. Place on a baking sheet, seam side down.

4 Repeat with remaining phyllo until all of the crab mixture is used. (The dumplings can be prepared in advance. Cover the baking sheets with plastic wrap and keep in the refrigerator. The baking time may need to be increased to 15 minutes if the dumplings are very cold.)

5 Lightly brush the tops of the dumplings with any remaining oil mixture and sprinkle with the sesame seeds. Bake until crisp and golden, about 12 to 13 minutes. Shred the tops of the green onions for garnish, and serve warm with dipping sauce.

PER SERVING: 3 g protein, 2 g total fat, 0 g saturated fat, 7 mg cholesterol, 9 g carbohydrates, 1 g fibre.

SAVOURY TREAT

Pair calcium-rich sesame seeds with vitamin D-packed salmon to reduce PMS symptoms. A study by the Archives of Internal Medicine found women with the highest intake of those two nutrients lowered their risk of getting PMS symptoms by 30 to 40 percent.

LIGHT TOUCH
Unlike puff pastry, phyllo is low in fat and calories. One sheet contains 2 grams of fat; only a light brushing of oil is needed to stick the pastry edges together and give a golden-brown sheen and crisp texture.

SMOKED SALMON CANAPÉS

Party fare doesn't have to be a minefield of fatty foods and fast-acting carbohydrates. These elegant hors d'oeuvres offer a delectable bite of smoked salmon (a source of protein and omega-3s), moistened with a light, lemony vinaigrette.

	24 slices cocktail rye bread	
2 tbsp	lemon juice	30 mL
2 tbsp	brewed black tea or vodka	30 mL
1 tbsp	extra-virgin olive oil	15 mL
2 tsp	Dijon mustard	10 mL
	Freshly ground pepper to taste	
8 ounces	sliced smoked salmon, finely chopped	250 g
¼ cup	finely diced red onion	60 mL
3 tbsp	chopped fresh dill, plus sprigs for garnish	45 mL
2 tbsp	drained capers, rinsed and coarsely chopped	30 mL

84
calories per 2 canapés

1 Preheat the oven to 325°F (160°C). Coat a baking sheet with nonstick spray. Arrange the cocktail rye bread slices in a single layer on the baking sheet. Spray the tops of slices lightly with nonstick spray. Bake the slices just until crisp, 12 to 15 minutes.

2 Whisk the lemon juice, tea (or vodka), oil, mustard, and pepper in a medium bowl. Add the smoked salmon, onion, dill and capers. Toss to mix well.

3 Shortly before serving, mound about 1 tbsp of topping on each slice of toast. Garnish each with a dill sprig.

PER SERVING: 5 g protein, 3 g total fat, 0 g saturated fat, 4 mg cholesterol, 9 g carbohydrates, 1 g fibre.

Make-ahead

◖ **Both the topping and toasts can be made early in the day. Refrigerate the topping, covered, for up to 8 hours. Store the toasts in an airtight container at room temperature.**

TURKEY & LENTIL PÂTÉ

SERVES 12

This coarse-textured pâté, deliciously flavoured with garlic and fresh cilantro, has considerably less fat than a traditional pâté. Serve with toasted slices of French baguette, plus some crisp vegetable sticks and crunchy radishes.

2 ounces	green lentils	60 g
2 tsp	canola oil	10 mL
	4 shallots, finely chopped	
	1 garlic clove, minced	
1 pound	ground turkey	500 g
¼ pound	turkey livers, chopped	125 g
3 tbsp	dry Marsala wine	45 mL
¼ cup	fresh cilantro	60 mL
	Salt and pepper	
	GARNISH	
	Sprigs of fresh cilantro	

87 calories per serving

1 Place the lentils in a saucepan, cover generously with water and bring to a boil. Simmer until tender, about 45 minutes. Drain well and set aside to cool.

2 Heat the oil in a large frying pan and sauté the shallots and garlic over medium-high heat until they have softened, about 2 minutes. Reduce the heat to medium and add the turkey and the livers. Cook, stirring, for 8 to 10 minutes.

3 Pour in the Marsala, bring to a boil and allow the mixture to boil for 1 to 2 minutes. Season lightly with salt and pepper. Transfer the mixture to a food processor. Add the cilantro and cooked lentils, and process for a few seconds to form a coarse paste consistency.

4 Spoon into 12 ramekins, pressing down well with the back of the spoon. Cover with plastic wrap and chill for 2 hours before serving. Garnish with fresh cilantro sprigs.

PER SERVING: 11 g protein, 3 g total fat, 1 g saturated fat, 67 mg cholesterol, 3 g carbohydrates, 1 g fibre.

SWAP *in Lentils*

LENTILS CAN SUBSTITUTE for meat in many recipes, such as hamburgers and meat loaf. Simply replace about half the meat with cooked lentils to cut fat and cholesterol while increasing fibre.

Cheese-flavoured nacho chips
100 calories = 7 chips. This has 5 g fat and 140 mg sodium.

100-CALORIE HANDFULS

How do crunchy handfuls compare in calories? Here, shown in actual size, is what 100 calories look like for five different types of munchies.

Of these five snacks, this one has the highest fat and the lowest sodium.

White-cheese flavoured popcorn
100 calories = 35 pieces (just under one cup). This has 1.3 g fat and 150 mg sodium.

Kettle-cooked potato chips
100 calories = 11 chips. This has 6 g fat and 80 mg sodium.

"Pop" chips (heat- & pressure-cooked potato chips)
100 calories = 19 chips. This has 3.5 g fat and 160 mg sodium.

Barbecue corn chips
100 calories = 18 chips. This has 1 g fat and 180 mg sodium.

Of these five snacks, this one has the lowest fat and the highest sodium.

SESAME SHRIMP & CRAB TOASTS

These toasts are usually deep-fried, but in this healthy version they are baked until golden.

140 calories per 2 triangles

TOPPING		
3 ounces	peeled raw shrimp, very finely chopped	90 g
3 ounces	fresh crab meat, flaked	90 g
	2 green onions, thinly sliced	
	1 large garlic clove, minced	
	½ small red pepper, seeded and diced	
½ tsp	finely grated lemon rind	3 mL
⅛ tsp	cayenne pepper	0.5 mL
1 tbsp	reduced-fat cream	15 mL
	Pepper to taste	
TOAST		
1 tbsp	reduced-fat cream	15 mL
	1 large egg	
	2 large slices multi-grain bread	
2 tsp	sesame seeds	10 mL
	Pepper to taste	
	Shredded green onions, to garnish	

1 Preheat the oven to 400°F (200°C). For the topping, place the shrimp, flaked crab meat, green onions, garlic, red pepper, lemon rind, cayenne pepper, and cream into a bowl and mix well to make a spreadable paste. Season with pepper and set aside.

2 Beat the cream and egg until smooth. Dip slices of multi-grain bread, coating both sides well, then put on a greased baking sheet. Spread the topping evenly over the bread, to the edges. Lightly brush the remaining egg and cream mixture over the surface of the shrimp and crab topping and sprinkle evenly with the sesame seeds.

3 Bake the toast for 20 to 25 minutes or until crisp and golden brown. Cut each slice of toast into 8 small triangles and serve immediately, while hot, garnished with shredded green onions.

PER SERVING: 12 g protein, 5 g total fat, 2 g saturated fat, 119 mg cholesterol, 11 g carbohydrates, 2 g fibre.

SWAP *Flavours*

For five-spice shrimp and water chestnut toast, omit the crab meat and double the shrimp. Season the mixture with ¼ tsp (1 mL) five-spice powder instead of the cayenne pepper and lemon rind. Instead of the red pepper, stir in 6 water chestnuts, very finely chopped, and 4 tsp (20 mL) chopped fresh coriander.

CRAB DIP WITH CRUDITÉS

This creamy dip is based on ingredients that can be kept in the pantry and rustled up quickly if guests drop by unexpectedly.

IN A PARTY MOOD?
For a **fancier** presentation, serve the crab dip on rounds of cucumber, cut about ½ inch (1 cm) thick. Garnish with thin strips of radish or water–cress leaves.

4 ounces	white crabmeat (1 can), drained	120 g
2 tbsp	light mayonnaise	30 mL
2 tbsp	plain low-fat yogurt	30 mL
1 tsp	tomato paste	5 mL
	Grated zest of 1 lime	
	6 sun-dried tomatoes, plumped	
	1 small pickle, finely chopped (optional)	
	Few drops of hot red pepper sauce, or to taste	
	CRUDITÉS	
	2 celery stalks, 1 medium cucumber, 1 small pineapple	

119 calories per serving

1 Place the crabmeat, mayonnaise, yogurt, tomato paste, lime zest, sun-dried tomatoes and pickle in a bowl and stir together thoroughly. Season with hot sauce to taste. Place the dip in a small serving bowl, cover and refrigerate while preparing the crudités.

2 Cut celery and cucumber into sticks. Cut the pineapple into wedges, trimming off the core. Arrange the celery, cucumber and pineapple on a platter with the bowl of dip. Divide into 4 servings and garnish with the pineapple leaves, if desired. Divide into 4 portions.

PER SERVING: 5 g protein, 4 g total fat, 1 g saturated fat, 3 mg cholesterol, 19 g carbohydrates, 2 g fibre.

TIP
Plump sun-dried tomatoes by covering with boiling water and letting sit for 15 minutes.

SMOKED TURKEY & APRICOT BITES

This tasty, healthy snack seems indulgent due to the combo of the sweet dried apricots and salty turkey bacon. Take care not to overcook the turkey bacon, which can become dry; a tangy mustard mixture adds moisture during cooking.

	24 dried apricots	
	Juice of 1 orange	
2 tsp	no-sugar-added orange marmalade	10 mL
2 tsp	Dijon mustard	10 mL
	6 slices turkey bacon	
1 tsp	olive oil	5 mL
	GARNISH	
	Chopped fresh parsley	

58 calories per 2 bites

1 Place apricots in a small bowl, pour the orange juice over, and toss so that the apricots are moistened completely (this will prevent them from burning).

2 Mix the marmalade and mustard. Spread each slice of turkey bacon with a little of the mixture; then, using scissors, cut it in half lengthwise. Cut each piece in half again, this time across the middle, making a total of 24 strips of turkey bacon.

3 Preheat a grill pan or turn on the oven broiler. Drain apricots. Wrap a strip of turkey bacon around each apricot and secure it with a toothpick. Arrange the turkey bites on the grill pan, then brush each with a little oil. Grill on each side until the turkey is just cooked, about 1 minute.

4 Pile the bites in a small, shallow bowl and sprinkle with chopped parsley. Serve hot.

PER SERVING: 2 g protein, 2 g total fat, 0 g saturated fat, 6 mg cholesterol, 10 g carbohydrates, 2 g fibre.

SWAP *Flavours*

INSTEAD OF THE MUSTARD and marmalade mixture, spread the turkey bacon with a little commercially prepared pesto. Cherry tomatoes can be used instead of dried apricots; they do not need to be moistened with orange juice.

Swap & Drop cocktail party

Words to live by: PACE YOURSELF

▶ Getting tipsy is a sure-fire way of loosening your inhibitions enough to ignore your priorities. Keep track of your drinks to count calories, yes, but also to keep consumption in check so that your diet resolve stays firm.

tip
Elaborate cocktails can torpedo your best intentions, so be very wary of them. Anything with a sugar rim, frozen, or containing multiple shots of liquor has strong potential to be a nasty caloric bomb.

party! planner

simple swaps

Order diet mixers, which save you about 100 calories per drink. **Or hold the mixer entirely.** Try a shot of vodka with a splash of water, on the rocks, the way your father likes it. **Dilute your white or rose wine** with sparkling water; your red wine with club soda. Sangria anyone? **Add lemon seltzer to your beer** for a low-cal shandy. **Skinny your pina colada** by using coconut water instead of coconut cream.

CALORIE-BUSTING STRATEGIES AT HOME OR AT THE BAR

• **Wait until your glass is empty** before getting a refill. Topping-up your drink is a great way to lose track of how much you're consuming. • **Two words: always alternate!** Having a glass of water or diet soda for each alcoholic drink is a good way to keep the calorie count under control while helping avoid unpleasant morning-after after effects. • **Start your evening with a glass of water** so that thirst doesn't drive you to drain the first glass quickly. • **Use a light hand on liquor.** Use less tequila and more ice in your Margarita. Make your second gin & tonic gin-free... You get the idea! • **Load up your glass** with ice cubes and fresh fruit.

Marvelous Mixers
❖ Diet soda or tonic—0 cals
❖ Sugar-free syrups—0 cals
❖ A half-ounce (15 mL) of lemon or lime juice—10 cals
❖ Light lemonade—5 cals
❖ Light juices—around 50 cals

Winning ways to lighten your favourites:

Wine
(6 ounces)—
145 cals
Wine spritzer (4 ounces wine: 2 ounces club soda)—95 cals

Beer
(12 ounces/350 mL)—
150 to 200 cals
Light beer (12 ounces/350 mL)—95 to 135 cals

Margarita
(8 ounces/240 mL)—
280 cals
Skinnygirl Skinnymini Margarita
(6.5-ounce/200 mL)—
160 cals

Screwdriver
(8 ounces/240 mL)—
190 cals
Vodka and Crystal Light—100 cals

Gin & tonic
(7 ounces/
200 mL)—200 cals
Gin & soda with a twist—100 cals

White Russian—425 cals
Black Russian—125 cals

TUSCAN BEAN CROSTINI

MAKES 22 CROSTINI

Here's a delicious snack to be enjoyed hot or at room temperature—toasted slices of baguette topped with a creamy white bean purée flavoured with garlic and thyme, and finished with colourful slices of tomato and fresh herbs.

61 calories per crostini

2 tsp	olive oil	10 mL
	1 small onion, finely chopped	
	1 garlic clove, minced	
1 14-ounce	can cannellini (white kidney) beans, drained and rinsed	1 398-mL
2 tbsp	low-fat plain yogurt	30 mL
1 tbsp	chopped fresh thyme	15 mL
	1 thin baguette (10 ounces/300 g)	
	3 plum tomatoes, thinly sliced	
	Salt and pepper	
	GARNISH	
	Sprigs of fresh herbs	

1 Heat the oil in a small frying pan, add the onion and garlic, then cook gently until softened, stirring occasionally, about 10 minutes.

2 Meanwhile, place the cannellini beans in a bowl and mash with a potato masher or fork. Remove the onion and garlic from the heat and stir in the mashed beans, yogurt, and thyme. Season lightly with salt and pepper and mix well. Keep warm while preparing the toasts.

3 Turn on the oven broiler. Cut the crusty ends off the baguette and discard, then cut the loaf into 22 equal slices, ½-inch (1-cm) thick. Toast the bread slices on both sides under the broiler. (The toasts and the bean mixture can be made in advance, left to cool to room temperature, then kept separately in airtight containers.)

4 To serve, spread some bean mixture over each slice of toast, top with a tomato slice and garnish with fresh herb sprigs.

PER SERVING 2.5 g protein, 1 g total fat, 0 g saturated fat, 0 mg cholesterol, 11 g carbohydrates, 2 g fibre.

SWAP
Flavours

Instead of cannellini beans, try chickpeas. Or top the bean mixture with grilled zucchini slices, lightly cooked button mushrooms, or halved cherry tomatoes. You can also replace the thyme with basil, parsley, oregano, or sage.

TIP
Canned beans are high in sodium, but you can slash it by about 40 percent just by draining them. A 30-second rinse reduces it by another 3 percent.

SWAP & DROP

GOOD

116 *calories*

BETTER

83 *calories*

WARM ARTICHOKE & BEAN DIP

SERVES 8

1 can cannellini (white kidney) beans, drained and rinsed

14 ounce/398 mL artichoke hearts (1 can), drained and rinsed

3 garlic cloves, minced

1 tbsp/15 mL reduced-fat mayonnaise

Pinch of cayenne pepper

Freshly ground pepper to taste

²/₃ cup plus 2 tbsp (80 g) grated Parmesan cheese

¼ cup/60 mL chopped fresh parsley

1 tsp/5 mL grated lemon zest

1 Preheat the oven to 400°F (200°C). Coat a medium baking dish with nonstick spray.

2 Place the beans, artichoke hearts, garlic, mayonnaise, cayenne, and black pepper in a food processor. Process until almost smooth, stopping to scrape down the sides of the bowl once or twice. Transfer to a medium bowl. Stir in ²/₃ cup of the Parmesan, parsley and lemon zest. Scrape into the baking dish and smooth with a spatula. Sprinkle with the remaining 2 tablespoons Parmesan.

3 Bake the dip, uncovered, until heated through, 20 to 25 minutes.

PER SERVING: 7 g protein, 3 g total fat, 2 g saturated fat, 7 mg cholesterol, 16 g carbohydrates, 5 g fibre.

SPICY DATE, APPLE & CHEESE DIP

SERVES 8

1 tsp/5 mL ground cardamom

1 extra-large tart apple, peeled, cored and coarsely chopped

¼ cup/60 mL chopped dates

1 tsp/5 mL ground cinnamon

¼ tsp/1 mL ground ginger

⅓ cup/75 mL water

8 ounces/250 g light cream cheese (or Neufchâtel) at room temperature

CRUDITÉS

Carrot, celery, and cucumber sticks; fresh pineapple and apple wedges; seedless grapes; strawberries

1 Mix the apple, dates, cardamom, cinnamon, and ginger in a medium saucepan, then add the water. Bring the mixture to a boil over medium heat, stirring occasionally.

2 Reduce the heat to low and simmer, uncovered, until the apple is tender and the dates are pulpy, about 10 minutes. Stir occasionally to prevent the mixture from sticking. Remove from heat and let cool.

3 Stir the cream cheese in a medium bowl until creamy, then blend in the fruit mixture. Cover and refrigerate until serving time. (It will keep in the refrigerator for up to 3 days.) Serve in a shallow bowl surrounded with an assortment of fruit and vegetable crudités.

PER SERVING: 3 g protein, 5 g total fat, 3 g saturated fat, 16 mg cholesterol, 8 g carbohydrates, 1 g fibre.

SMOKED SALMON & FRESH DILL POTATO SKINS SERVES 8

Brushing potato skins with a little olive oil and butter and then baking them reduces the fat content of this popular restaurant appetizer.

	8 small (5-ounce/150-g) baking potatoes	
1 tbsp	olive oil, divided	15 mL
1 tbsp	butter	15 mL
4 ounces	smoked salmon	120 g
1 tbsp	lemon juice	15 mL
½ cup	light sour cream	125 mL
1 tbsp	capers, drained and chopped	15 mL
2 tbsp	chopped fresh dill	30 mL
	Salt and pepper	
	GARNISH	
	Small sprigs of fresh dill	

167 calories per 4 skins

1 Preheat the oven to 400°F (200°C). Scrub and dry the potatoes. Thread them onto metal skewers (they cook more quickly). Brush the skins with half the oil, then sprinkle with a little salt. Arrange on a baking tray and bake until tender, about 1 to 1 ½ hours.

2 Remove potatoes from skewers and cut them in half lengthwise. Scoop out the flesh, leaving a layer next to the skin about ½ inch (1 cm) thick. Cut each piece in half lengthwise again, and place flesh side up on a clean baking tray.

3 Melt butter with the remaining oil and season lightly with salt and pepper. Lightly brush this mixture on the potato flesh. Return to the oven and bake until golden and crisp, about 12 to 15 minutes.

4 Cut the smoked salmon into fine strips; sprinkle with lemon juice. Mix together sour cream, capers, and chopped dill in a bowl, then stir in the salmon.

5 Allow the potato skins to cool for a minute, then top each with a little of the salmon and sour cream mixture. Garnish with a small sprig of dill and serve warm.

PER SERVING 6 g protein, 5 g total fat, 2 g saturated fat, 12 mg cholesterol, 26 g carbohydrates, 4 g fibre.

SHOPPING

Check the date

"Best before" dates can be changed by stores, so check the "packaged on" date to know how fresh the food really is. One or the other is required on every food expected to expire within 90 days, according to Canadian law.

3

MAIN MEALS

3 Main Meals Recipes that bring it all to the table: great taste and nutritional goodness

Treating supper like you would a good friend just might be your best strategy to eating well and losing weight. **Be thoughtful.** *People who think ahead about what to serve on busy weeknights are much more likely to plan balanced meals. You save money, too, when you include a few super-quick or make-ahead suppers for those nights when you're too tired to cook.* **Relax and enjoy the time you spend together.** *Schedule enough time for supper so that you don't feel rushed. Sit down at a table cleared of distractions (except, of course, your kids!), and make a point of really tasting each bite.* **Make conversation.** *Sharing thoughts, a joke you heard, and the day's tidbits around the table brings families closer. It also slows you down enough for your body to signal that your stomach is full before you decide to load up on seconds. When eating alone, try putting your cutlery down between bites. Try to stay "in the moment." Slower eating also aids digestion.* **Take a post-supper stroll.** *As a proverb advises, "After dinner rest a while, after supper walk a mile."*

What's for dinner?

Planning your evening meal begins with a mindful trip down the grocery store aisle. It's a giant step towards eating healthier

"The greatest thing in the world is not so much where we are, but in what direction we are moving."

—*Oliver Wendell Holmes*

Prepared foods are part of our busy lifestyle, and that's not going to change. But you can swap in better choices for ones often laden with unneccesarily higher salt, fat, and calories. When shopping, take your time to do comparisons.

Filling your house with food may sound like strange diet advice, but a bare cupboard is just asking for trouble. No matter how bare your fridge is, chances are there's a bag of chips from last week's party lurking somewhere. And if that's all that's around, you're going to grab it if you get hungry enough.

By keeping plenty of healthy foods around you can make sure the best choices are right in front of you when you open the refrigerator or cupboard door. With the right selection of essentials on hand, you can always put together a simple and delicious meal.

So make sure that your every trip to the supermarket is a time to become better informed and to stock up on dinner essentials. Take time to compare nutritional labels and make good choices for yourself and your family. We've done some comparison shopping to help get you started:

Salad savvy. Save 125 calories by choosing two tablespoons (30 mL) low-fat vinaigrette over creamy Caesar dressing. Swap out croutons for crunchy veggies.

Leanest cuts of meat

▶ The leanest cuts of beef are: eye of round, inside round, sirloin tip, top sirloin, flank, strip loin, cross rib, and outside round.

▶ The tenderloin is the leanest cut of pork. Other lean cuts are: boneless loin roast, boneless loin chops, and boneless, extra-lean ham.

TRY THIS!

Put 3 rubber bands around your wrist every morning. That's how many 500 mL bottles of water you should drink during the day to rev up your metabolism. At least, that's what German researchers found when they got 14 participants to drink about 500 mL of water. The volunteers' metabolic rate—how quickly they burned calories—jumped a third within 10 minutes of drinking the water and remained high for another 30 or 40 minutes. The researchers estimated that, over a year, increasing your water consumption by 1.5 litres a day would burn an extra 17,400 calories, or about 5 pounds' worth. And since much of the increased metabolic rate is due to the body's efforts to heat the water, drink it ice cold.

Soup swap. Choose chicken noodle over cream of broccoli; for one 280-gram serving, you'll save 50 calories and 7 grams of fat. Generally, clear soups are your best bet. (Or make your own "creamy" soups using a blender and adding cooked potatoes or lentils.)

Fish friends. Battered frozen fish tends to be a dieting no-no. Check out alternatives, such as breaded fish fingers, which can trim both calories and fat by more–sometimes much more–than half.

Here's another fishy idea: if you normally have beef a couple of times a week, change 1 meal to fish. A 3-ounce (75-gram) broiled steak has 230 calories and 14 grams of fat. Compare that to the same-sized serving of broiled cod at just 80 calories and 1 gram of fat. You save 150 calories and 13 grams of fat.

Pizza perfect. In general, avoid thick-crust meat lovers' pizza, choosing instead a thin crust with vegetables (when ordering takeout, ask for half the cheese and double the veggies to slash about 500 calories from your meal). But check your favourites, and they may surprise you: one serving of Delissio's Rising Crust Hawaiian Pizza has significantly less fat (10 grams) than its Crispy Flatbread Pizza (19 grams).

Red vs. white. Yummy alfredo sauce has 180 calories in a ½-cup serving. Use tomato sauce instead to save 100 calories.

Are you !#*@%?& kidding me?

Get more sleep; lose more weight. When you get limited deep sleep, the brain thinks you're running low on energy, so it increases your appetite. A Quebec study showed that people who slept 5 to 6 hours each night were 69 percent more likely to be overweight or obese than those sleeping nine to 10 hours. Sleep deprived? Try swapping 1 hour of "inactive wakefulness", like TV, for one more hour in the sack.

SWAP IN FRUIT
Adding fresh fruit to a meat dish is an easy way to include more vitamins and fibre. Sliced pears, halved kumquats, orange segments, or pineapple chunks could be used in place of the apple.

"Eat food. Not too much. Mostly plants," advises food writer Michael Pollan, and it's wise to follow his advice when planning your main meal. You can enjoy meats and seafood, of course, but always remember to visualize your portion size. The rules of thumb are: a serving of meat or poultry the size of a deck of cards; a chequebook-sized serving of fish; or a tennis ball serving of legumes, such as chickpeas and beans. Add another tennis ball's worth of starch and as many veggies as you wish.

CIDER-BRAISED HAM WITH SWEET POTATO

SERVES 4

High-fibre sweet potatoes and lean ham are combined in this tasty low-fat dish.

211 calories per serving

1 cup plus 1 tbsp	apple cider	250 plus 15 mL
1 tbsp	Dijon mustard	15 mL
1 tbsp	peeled, finely chopped fresh ginger	15 mL
½ tsp	ground cloves	2 mL
	1 medium sweet potato, peeled and thinly sliced	
1 pound	extra lean ham steak	500 g
	1 Granny Smith apple, peeled, cored and cut into 12 wedges	
1 tbsp	cornstarch	15 mL
½ cup	green onions, green part only	75 g

1 Combine 1 cup (250 mL) of the cider, the mustard, ginger, and cloves in a large frying pan. Bring to a simmer. Add the sweet potato. Cover tightly and simmer until partially tender, or 15 minutes.

2 Add ham steak. Cover with sweet potato slices. Arrange apple wedges over the top. Cover and simmer until apples and potato are tender and ham is heated through, 10 to 15 minutes.

3 Using a slotted spoon, transfer ham, potato, and apple to plate. Cover with aluminium foil to keep warm.

4 Blend cornstarch and 1 tbsp (15 mL) cider in a small bowl. Stir a little of the hot pan liquid into the mixture until smooth. Add cornstarch mixture to pan. Cook over medium heat, stirring, until slightly thickened, about 1 minute.

5 Divide ham, sweet potato and apple between four plates. Spoon on sauce from the pan. Slice green onions diagonally and use as garnish.

PER SERVING: 18 g protein, 4 g total fat, 1 g saturated fat, 38 mg cholesterol, 25 g carbohydrates, 2 g fibre.

VEAL WITH HERBS

In this summery dish, the veal is pounded out ultra-thin, making it ultra-fast to cook.

1 pound	baby new potatoes, scrubbed	500 g
4 4-ounce	veal scallopini, pounded to 1/4-inch (0.5 cm) thickness	4 125-g
2 tbsp	flour	30 mL
1 tbsp	olive oil, divided	15 mL
2 tsp	unsalted butter, divided	10 mL
6 cups	baby leaf spinach	1.5 L
	Grated zest and juice of 1 lemon	
1/3 cup	dry white wine	75 mL
4 tbsp	chopped mixed fresh herbs, such as parsley, chervil, chives, tarragon	60 mL
	Salt and pepper, to taste	
	Lemon wedges, to garnish	

311 calories per serving

1 Cook the potatoes. Boil in a large saucepan until tender, about 15 minutes. Drain and remove.

2 Pat the veal dry. Dredge in flour seasoned with a little salt and pepper; shake off excess. Heat half the oil in a non-stick frying pan over medium heat. Add half the butter and heat until it foams, then add veal. Sauté until the juices run clear, about 2 to 3 minutes on each side. Remove and keep warm.

3 Add remaining oil to the potato saucepan, heat on low. Add potatoes and toss gently until coated. Add spinach in 4 batches, gently tossing so it wilts in the heat from the potatoes. Add lemon juice. Season lightly; stir gently to mix. Cover and keep warm while you make the sauce.

4 Return the frying pan to the heat and add wine. Heat to boiling, then stir vigorously to dislodge any browned bits. Boil until syrupy, about 1 minute, then season lightly. Remove from the heat and add remaining butter. Stir until melted.

5 Scatter mixed herbs over the veal; drizzle with sauce. Sprinkle lemon zest over the potatoes and spinach. Serve the vegetables alongside the veal, with lemon wedges for squeezing.

PER SERVING: 28 g protein, 9 g total fat, 3 g saturated fat, 82 mg cholesterol, 28 g carbohydrates, 4 g fibre.

SWAP IT OUT!

● ● ● Pork (or Turkey) Fillets with Mushrooms and Peppers

Lean pork or turkey fillets, pounded thin, can be cooked the same way. Add 2 seeded, thinly sliced green peppers and 1 cup (250 mL) sliced button mushrooms to the juices in the pan. Stir and toss over high heat for 2 minutes, then add 1 crushed garlic clove and the white wine. Cook until the liquid is reduced and syrupy. Season with salt and pepper to taste. Pour the wine sauce over the pork or turkey (omit the mixed herbs) and serve with boiled new potatoes.

INGREDIENT INTEL
This dish is especially rich in **B vitamins**: B6 in the veal and the new potatoes, B3 and B12 in the veal.

BEEF SALAD WITH MUSTARD VINAIGRETTE

SERVES 4

Lean roasted tenderloin of beef makes this a succulent salad for entertaining.

1 pound	beef tenderloin	500 g
1 tsp	olive oil	5 mL
¾ pound	new potatoes, scrubbed	375 g
¼ pound	French or regular green beans, halved	125 g
½ cup	shelled fresh or frozen peas	125 mL
	1 large leek, finely chopped	
2 tbsp	snipped fresh chives	30 mL
	VINAIGRETTE	
1 ½ tbsp	olive oil	20 mL
1 tbsp	red wine vinegar	15 mL
1 ½ tsp	Dijon mustard	7 mL
	Pinch of sugar and salt and pepper, to taste	

318 calories per serving

1 Preheat oven to 450°F (230°C). Rub the fillet with the olive oil and set on a rack in a roasting pan. Roast for 15 minutes for rare beef, or up to 25 minutes for well done. Meanwhile, whisk together the ingredients for the vinaigrette in a large mixing bowl.

2 Remove the beef from the oven and leave to stand for 5 minutes, then cut into thin slices against the grain. Add to the dressing and leave to cool.

3 Cook the potatoes in a saucepan of boiling water until tender, about 15 minutes. Drain well. When cool enough to handle, cut in half or into thick slices and add to the beef.

4 Drop green beans into another pan of boiling water and cook for 1 minute. Add peas and cook until the vegetables are tender, about 3 minutes. Drain and refresh briefly under cold running water, then add to the beef and potatoes. Toss well. Cover and refrigerate for 30 minutes.

5 About 15 minutes before serving, stir leeks and chives into the salad. Let sit outside fridge.

PER SERVING: 24 g protein, 14 g total fat, 4 g saturated fat, 60 mg cholesterol, 25 g carbohydrates, 4 g fibre.

1 MORE IDEA

● ● ● **Spicy Pork Fillet Salad**

Mix 1 tbsp (15 mL) sugar, 1 tsp (5 mL) celery salt, 1 tsp (5 mL) garlic powder, ½ tsp (2 mL) ground ginger, ½ tsp (2 mL) ground allspice, ½ tsp (2 mL) paprika and 1 tsp (5 mL) cider vinegar to make a thick, grainy paste. Spread this over a 1-pound (500-g) pork tenderloin, then leave to marinate for up to 8 hours. Roast the pork in a preheated 400°F (200°C) oven until cooked through, about 30 minutes. Remove from the oven and leave to cool. Meanwhile, place 1 cup (250 mL) basmati rice in a saucepan of boiling water and cook until tender, about 20 minutes. Drain well and set aside to cool. To assemble the salad, cut the pork into cubes and mix with the rice and ½ cup (125 mL) fresh pineapple chunks, 1 large diced mango, and 2 celery stalks, diced. Garnish with 2 tbsp (30 mL) chopped parsley and ½ tsp (2 mL) paprika.

Swap & Drop

cool-weather party

tempting toddy

4 cups (1 L) pineapple juice, 1 cup (250 mL) sliced fresh ginger, 1 tbsp (15 mL) honey, 1 cinnamon stick, 8 cloves, ¼ tsp (1 mL) pepper. Combine in a pot, bring to a boil and simmer for 10 minutes. Strain and serve. Serves 4. (152 calories per serving)

party! planner

"The great thing about snow is it makes your lawn look as good as your neighbours'."
—Author unknown

Menu

Smoked Salmon Canapés
(page 122) • *This traditional starter has a couple of calorie-reduced twists.*

Beef in Red Wine & Brandy
(page 157) • *The perfect dish for a small gathering, its slow cooking fills the kitchen with warmth and a delicious aroma. Serve with boiled potatoes and a warmed loaf of crusty bread. For a large gathering you might prefer* **cider-braised ham** *(page 143), a crowd-pleaser for all ages.*

Lightened-Up Chocolate Mousse
(page 221). • *A decadent-tasting dessert with a creamy finish.*

TIPS TO AVOID A WINTER WAISTLINE

• Take advantage of long nights by getting a good sleep, which helps you avoid overeating. • Practice your snowball pitching; or shovel some! • Don't hang out at the buffet table; chat in a foodless room. • Keep your hands busy. • Keep your mind occupied. • Chew gum!

HOT CHILI CHOCOLATE *for two*

2 cups (500 mL) 1% milk
½ tsp (2 mL) vanilla extract
½ tsp (2 mL) cinnamon
¼ tsp (1 mL) cayenne pepper
2 tbsp (30 mL) dark chocolate chips or 1 ounce (30 g) bitter-sweet chocolate, grated

Heat milk over medium heat. Add vanilla, cinnamon and cayenne pepper. Stir in dark chocolate chips (or chopped bittersweet chocolate) until melted. Pour into mugs.

SERVES 2. Per serving: 196 calories, 12 g protein, 11 g fat, 7 g saturated fat, 10 mg cholesterol, 19 g carbohydrates, 3 g fibre, 146 mg sodium.

Splashes of colour Extra cranberries crowding the fridge? Brighten your cold-weather baking by adding a handful of cranberries when baking apples or pear pies, crisps and crumbles, as well as scones, muffins, and loaves. Here's another idea: top greens with fennel slices and clementine sections. Drizzle with olive oil and sprinkle on pomegranate seeds.

Holiday Smoothie
This makes a tasty alternative to eggnog. Garnish it with a pretty rim of crushed candy cane.

SERVES 4. Per serving: 114 calories, 8 g protein, 1 g fat, 1 g saturated fat, 6 mg cholesterol, 19 g carbohydrates, 1 g fibre, 99 mg sodium.

Blend the following:
1½ cups (375 mL) skim milk
1½ cups (375 mL) low-fat vanilla yogurt
1½ cups (375 mL) ice cubes
5 peppermint leaves, torn
1 tbsp (15 mL) ground cinnamon
A few drops peppermint extract (optional)

SIRLOIN STEAKS WITH PORT SAUCE

In this robust dish, pan juices transform into an instant sauce.

1 pound	new potatoes, large ones halved	500 g
1 tsp	olive oil	5 mL
1 cup	large mushrooms, quartered	250 mL
1 cup	sugar snap or snow peas	250 mL
	1 large red pepper, seeded and cut into thin strips	
²/₃ cup	low-sodium beef or vegetable stock, divided	150 mL
1 tbsp	Worcestershire sauce	15 mL
1 tsp	each, Dijon mustard and brown sugar	5 mL
4 5-ounce	thin sirloin steaks, fat trimmed	4-150 g
1 tsp	butter	5 mL
	1 shallot, finely chopped	
	2 garlic cloves, crushed	
4 tbsp	port	60 mL
	Salt and pepper, to taste	

343
calories per serving

1 Bring potatoes to a boil, then reduce the heat and simmer for 10 to 12 minutes. Meanwhile, heat oil in a non-stick wok or large frying pan over medium-high heat. Add mushrooms, peas, and pepper strips, and stir-fry for 1 minute. Mix half of the broth with the Worcestershire sauce, mustard, and sugar, and stir into the vegetables. Reduce the heat and simmer gently for 3 minutes or until the vegetables are just tender, stirring frequently.

2 Season steaks on both sides with coarsely ground black pepper; set aside. Heat a grill pan. Meanwhile, drain cooked potatoes and add to vegetables. Stir gently; cover and keep warm.

3 Add butter to grill pan and turn heat to high. When the starts to foam, add steaks. When cooked to your preferred doneness, put the steaks onto warmed dinner plates. Keep warm.

4 Add shallot and garlic to the cooking juices in the pan and cook, stirring, over low heat for 1 minute. Pour in the port and increase the heat so the sauce is bubbling. Cook for about 1 minute, stirring. Pour in the remaining broth and boil 1 minute. Correct the seasoning. Spoon sauce over the steaks and serve immediately with the vegetables.

PER SERVING: 32 g protein, 9 g total fat, 3 g saturated fat, 83 mg cholesterol, 32 g carbohydrates, 4 g fibre.

SWAP
Flavours

You can substitute a **full-bodied red wine** for the port.

For a quick and fresh **vegetable stir-fry**, omit the Worcestershire sauce, mustard, and sugar, and just toss the vegetables with 2 tbsp (30 mL) chopped fresh chives before serving.

SWAP & DROP

GOOD

511 *calories*

BETTER

318 *calories*

ONE-POT STEAK & PASTA CASSEROLE
SERVES 4

1 tbsp/15 mL olive oil

1 pound/500 g lean sirloin steak, cut into ½-inch (1-cm) cubes

1 onion, chopped

1 28-ounce/796-mL can chopped tomatoes

2 tbsp/30 mL tomato paste

2 garlic cloves, crushed

3 cups/750 mL reduced-sodium beef or vegetable broth, divided

3 large carrots, sliced

4 celery stalks, sliced

1 small rutabaga, peeled and chopped

8 ounces/250 g fusilli pasta

1 tsp/5 mL oregano

Salt and pepper, to taste

1 Heat oil in a large Dutch oven over medium-high heat, then add beef. Brown the meat, stirring frequently. Use a slotted spoon to remove meat from the pan and pour off any grease.

2 Add onion to the pan and cook, stirring often, until softened, about 5 minutes. Then add tomatoes with their juice, tomato paste, garlic, and 2 cups (500 mL) of broth. Stir well and bring to a boil.

3 Return beef to the pan. Add carrots, celery, and rutabaga, and season lightly with salt and pepper. Cover and simmer gently until the meat is tender, about 1 hour.

4 Add pasta and oregano with the remaining broth. Bring the mixture to a simmer, then reduce the heat and cover the pan. Cook until the pasta is tender, 20 to 25 minutes. Serve immediately.

PER SERVING: 35 g protein, 10 g total fat, 2 g saturated fat, 64 mg cholesterol, 71 g carbohydrates, 8 g fibre.

AROMATIC BEEF CURRY
SERVES 6

2 tsp/10 mL canola oil

1 large onion, thinly sliced

½ cup/125 mL button mushrooms, sliced

1 pound/500 g sirloin steak, trimmed of fat, cut into strips

1 tsp/5 mL fresh ginger, peeled and chopped

2 garlic cloves, crushed

2 tsp/10 mL ground coriander

1 tsp/5 mL each crushed red pepper flakes, ground cardamom, turmeric, grated nutmeg

1 19-ounce/540-mL can chopped tomatoes

1 tsp/5 mL flour

1 tbsp/15 mL water

1 cup/250 mL plain low-fat yogurt

1 tbsp/15 mL honey

1 cup/250 mL spinach leaves

Juice of 1 lime

2 tbsp/30 mL chopped fresh cilantro

1 Heat oil in a large pan; add onion and mushrooms. Cook on high heat until onion slices begin to brown, about 2 minutes.

2 Add beef, ginger, garlic, and spices. Cook for 2 minutes, stirring, then add tomatoes. Combine flour with water and add to mixture. Bring to a boil, stirring. Stir in the yogurt and honey. Return to a boil then reduce heat, cover and simmer gently for 20 minutes.

3 Stir the spinach, lime juice, and cilantro into the curry and allow the leaves to wilt. Spoon curry over basmati rice (see recipe page 208) and garnish with additional fresh cilantro sprigs.

PER SERVING: 21 g protein, 6 g total fat, 2 g saturated fat, 26 mg cholesterol, 45 g carbohydrates, 2 g fibre.

SESAME PORK & NOODLE SALAD

SERVES 4

With its typical Asian flavours, this salad makes a delectable lunch or supper dish. For the best effect, cut the pepper, carrot, and green onions into strips that are about the same thickness as the noodles.

1 pound	pork tenderloin	500 g
2 tsp	grated fresh ginger	10 mL
1 large garlic clove, finely chopped		
1 tsp	dark sesame oil	5 mL
3 tbsp	light soy sauce	45 mL
2 tbsp	dry sherry	30 mL
2 tsp	rice vinegar	10 mL
8 ounces	fine Chinese egg noodles	250 g
1 red pepper, seeded and cut into matchstick strips		
1 large carrot, cut into matchstick strips		
6 green onions, cut into matchstick strips		
1 cup	snow peas	250 mL
1 tbsp	sesame seeds	15 mL
2 tsp	canola oil	10 mL

443 calories per serving

INGREDIENT INTEL

In the past, **pork** has had a reputation for being rather fatty, but this is certainly no longer the case. Over the last 20 years, in response to consumer demands, farmers have been breeding leaner pigs. Pork now contains considerably less fat, and it also contains higher levels of the "good" polyunsaturated fats. The average fat content of lean pork is very similar to that of a skinless chicken breast.

1 Trim all visible fat from the pork. Cut the pork across into slices about 2 inches (5 cm) thick, then cut each slice into thin strips.

2 Combine the ginger, garlic, sesame oil, soy sauce, sherry, and vinegar in a bowl. Add the pork strips and toss to coat, then leave to marinate while you prepare the other ingredients.

3 Place the noodles in a large mixing bowl and pour over enough boiling water to cover generously. Leave to soak until tender, about 4 minutes, or according to the package instructions. Drain well and place back into the bowl. Add the red pepper, carrot, and green onions.

4 Drop the snow peas into a pan of boiling water and cook until just tender but still crisp, about 1 minute. Drain and refresh under cold running water. Add the snow peas to the noodle and vegetable mixture and toss to mix. Set aside.

5 Toast the sesame seeds in a large frying pan over medium heat until golden, about 1 to 2 minutes, stirring constantly. Remove the seeds from the pan and set aside. Heat the oil in the frying pan, increase the heat slightly, and add the pork with its marinade. Stir-fry until the pork is no longer pink, about 4 to 5 minutes.

6 Add the strips of pork and any cooking juices to the noodle and vegetable mixture, and stir gently to combine. Divide among 4 shallow bowls, sprinkle with the toasted sesame seeds and serve.

PER SERVING: 34 g protein, 11 g total fat, 3 g saturated fat, 119 mg cholesterol, 51 g carbohydrates, 4 g fibre.

SWAP IT OUT!

● ● ● **Sesame Pork & Rice Noodle Salad**

Use 8 ounces (250 g) rice noodles instead of egg noodles. Soak them as in the main recipe, then mix with the red pepper, carrot, and green onions.

STIR-FRIED BEEF WITH VERMICELLI

Tangy tamarind and lemongrass infuse this Thai-inspired dish.

INGREDIENT INTEL
Gram for gram, **chili peppers** are richer in vitamin C than citrus fruits, such as oranges. However, you would have to eat substantially more of these spice veggies than you are likely to eat!

1 tsp	tamarind paste	5 mL
4 tbsp	boiling water	60mL
2 tbsp	reduced-salt soy sauce	30mL
2 tsp	sesame oil	10mL
1 tbsp	rice wine (sake or mirin) or sherry	15mL
3 ½ ounces	rice vermicelli	100 g
1 tbsp	sunflower oil	15 mL
½ pound	lean steak, cut into strips	220 g
	1 small onion, cut into wedges	
2 tsp	chopped lemongrass	10 mL
	1 fresh red chili pepper, seeded and chopped	
	2 large garlic cloves, crushed	
½ cup	snow peas, halved diagonally	80 g
	6 baby corn, sliced	
¼ pound shiitake or button mushrooms, sliced		100 g

1 In a small bowl, combine tamarind paste and boiling water and let soak for 10 minutes, stirring frequently. Press through a sieve and mix the resulting liquid with the soy sauce. Soak vermicelli in boiling water for 4 minutes, or according to the package instructions. Then drain, rinse under cold running water and set aside to drain thoroughly.

2 Heat sunflower oil in a wok or very large frying pan and stir-fry beef over a high heat for about 3 minutes or until cooked. Use a slotted spoon to remove the beef and set it aside.

3 Add onion, lemongrass, chili, and garlic to the wok and stir-fry over high heat for 1 minute. Add the snow peas, baby corn, and mushrooms, and continue stir-frying for 2 minutes. Return the beef to the wok. Add the tamarind liquid and the vermicelli and stir for about 1 minute to heat through. Serve at once.

PER SERVING: 29 g protein, 21 g total fat, 4 g saturated fat, 53 mg cholesterol, 45 g carbohydrates, 4 g fibre.

SWAP IT OUT!
You can use strips of chicken breast instead of beef. Other vegetables that work well in the stir-fry include strips of red or green pepper, sliced canned water chestnuts, chopped or shredded green onions, and bean sprouts.

BRAISED PORK WITH CRANBERRIES

SERVES 4

Cranberries add a tangy undertone to this dish.

380 calories per serving

½ cup	sugar	125 mL
1 tsp	dried rosemary, minced	5 mL
1 tsp	salt	5 mL
½ tsp	pepper	2 mL
½ tsp	ground ginger	2 mL
1 pound	well-trimmed pork tenderloin, halved crosswise	450 g
1 tbsp	olive oil	15 mL
12 cloves garlic, peeled		
8 green onions, cut into 2-inch (5-cm) lengths		
4 carrots, cut into matchsticks		
12 ounces	fresh or frozen cranberries	340 g
⅔ cup orange juice		
1 bay leaf		

1 Preheat the oven to 350°F (180°C). In a large bowl, stir together ¼ cup of the sugar, rosemary, salt, pepper, and ginger. Add the pork, and turn to coat with the spice mixture.

2 In a non-stick Dutch oven or ovenproof casserole, heat the oil over medium-high heat. Lift the pork from the spice mixture and add to the pan along with the garlic. Cook the pork for 2 minutes per side, or until it is richly browned. Transfer the pork to a plate.

3 Add the green onions and carrots to the pan and cook for 3 minutes, or until the carrots begin to colour. Stir the remaining ¼ cup sugar, the cranberries, orange juice, and bay leaf into the pan; bring to a boil.

4 Return the pork to the pan; reduce to a simmer, cover, and transfer to the oven. Bake for 30 minutes, or until the pork is cooked through but still juicy.

5 Lift the pork from the pan and slice. Remove and discard the bay leaf from the sauce. Serve the pork with vegetables and sauce on top.

PER SERVING: 26 g protein, 8 g total fat, 2 g saturated fat, 74 mg cholesterol, 53 g carbohydrates, 7 g fibre.

2 MORE IDEAS

● ● ● **A tangy appetizer**

Mix softened goat cheese, chopped dried cranberries, dried basil, and black pepper to taste. Spread on toasted baguette and top with pecan halves.

● ● ● **Need a vegetarian dinner?**

Halve a squash and bake until cooked. Fill with a mixture of sautéed onion, toasted whole-grain bread cubes, grated cheddar cheese, fresh cranberries, and chopped walnuts. Bake until heated through.

SWAP & DROP
DINING OUT

SWAP THIS

FOR THAT

BOSTON PIZZA

Baked Chipotle Bacon Penne
(penne in bacon and alfredo sauce with mushrooms, green onion, tomato, cheddar, and pizza mozzarella)

1,430 calories

88 g fat (40 g saturated)

2,740 mg sodium

Baked Seven-Cheese Ravioli
(pasta, various cheeses, and Bolognese or Pomodoro sauce)

490 calories

26 g fat (15 g saturated)

850 mg sodium

EAST SIDE MARIO'S

Linguine Chicken Tetrazzini
(chicken breast, mushrooms, garlic, and tomatoes in alfredo sauce, with side Caesar salad and garlic homeloaf)

1,730 calories

55 g fat (18 g saturated)

2,590 mg sodium

Side Serving of Pasta with Napolitana Sauce
(with a side vegetable soup)

440 calories

9 g fat (1 g saturated)

1,360 mg sodium

THE KEG

Bruschetta
(Ciabatta bread topped with tomato basil salsa, bocconcini, and parmesan cheese)

1,145 calories

59 g fat (22 g saturated)

1,384 mg sodium

Shrimp Cocktail
(tiger shrimp with a martini cocktail sauce)

127 calories

1 g fat (0 g saturated)

823 mg sodium

THE KEG

8 oz. Sirloin Oscar
(steak with shrimp, scallops, asparagus, and Bearnaise sauce)

917 calories

67 g fat (11 g saturated)

1,110 mg sodium

8 oz. Sirloin Classic
(steak comes with salad, vegetables, and mushrooms)

440 calories

21 g fat (6 g saturated)

714 mg sodium

FIVE-SPICE PORK

SERVES 4

The Asian technique of stir-frying is perfect; it preserves veggies' nutritive value, puts meals on the table in a hurry, and uses little oil.

427 calories per serving

1 pound	pork tenderloin, trimmed of fat, cut into 2-inch (5-cm) strips	500 g
8 ounces	medium Chinese egg noodles	250 g
1 tsp	canola oil	5 mL
	1 large onion, finely chopped	
	1 large garlic clove, crushed	
1 tbsp	five-spice powder	15 mL
1 cup	sugar snap or snow peas	250 mL
	2 large red peppers (or 1 red and 1 yellow or orange), seeded and thinly sliced	
½ cup	hot reduced-sodium vegetable broth	125 mL
	Salt and pepper	
	GARNISH	
	Fresh cilantro leaves	

1 Cook the noodles in a saucepan of boiling water for 4 minutes, or cook or soak them according to the package instructions. Drain the noodles well and set aside.

2 While the noodles are cooking, heat a wok or a large heavy-based frying pan until hot. Add the oil and swirl to coat the wok, then add the onion and garlic and stir-fry for 1 minute. Add the five-spice powder and stir-fry for another minute.

3 Add the pork strips to the wok and stir-fry for 3 minutes. Add the sugar snap peas and the peppers and stir-fry for a further 2 minutes. Pour in the broth, stir well, and bring to a boil.

4 Add the noodles to the wok and stir and toss until all the ingredients are well combined, about 2 to 3 minutes. Season with salt and pepper to taste, sprinkle with cilantro, and serve immediately.

PER SERVING: 34 g protein, 8 g total fat, 3 g saturated fat, 119 mg cholesterol, 55 g carbohydrates, 6 g fibre.

SWAP
Down calories

To reduce the fat content of this dish even further, use just ½ pound (250 g) pork and add ½ pound (250 g) firm tofu. Drain the tofu well and cut it into 1-inch (2.5-cm) cubes, then add in Step 3 with the sugar snap peas and peppers. Add 2 tbsp (30 mL) light soy sauce with the stock.

TENDER TECHNIQUE

The technique of simmering the sirloin steak in the tomato and broth mixture is called "moist cooking". Moist heat helps to tenderize even the leanest cuts of meat

BEEF IN RED WINE & BRANDY

Slow cooking gives this traditional casserole its rich flavour. For an everyday version, you can swap 3 cups (750 mL) reduced-salt beef stock or light ale for the wine.

1 pound	lean stewing beef	500 g
2 tbsp	sunflower oil	30 mL
	1 large onion, sliced	
½ pound	baby carrots	250 g
½ pound	baby parsnips	250 g
½ pound	button mushrooms	250 g
	1 garlic clove, finely chopped	
	1 bottle full-bodied red wine	
	Grated rind and juice of 1 orange	
	1 sprig fresh thyme	
	1 sprig fresh rosemary	
	1 bay leaf	
	pepper to taste	
½ pound	shelled fresh broad beans or frozen broad beans, thawed	200 g
2 tbsp	chopped parsley	30 mL
4 tbsp	brandy (optional)	60 mL

538 calories per serving

INGREDIENT INTEL
Along with its other nutritional benefits, **beef** is a useful source of vitamin D, which is found in few foods. Vitamin D is essential for the absorption of calcium, and helps in forming and maintaining healthy bones.

1 Preheat the oven to 300°F (150°C). Dice the beef ½-inch (1-cm) thick.

2 Heat the sunflower oil in a large flameproof casserole dish. Add the sliced onion and cook over medium-high heat for about 5 minutes or until softened and beginning to brown.

3 Add the stewing beef to the casserole dish and fry for another 5 minutes, stirring frequently, until the pieces of beef are browned on all sides. Stir in the baby carrots, parsnips, button mushrooms, and garlic.

4 Pour in the red wine, then stir in the orange rind and juice, thyme, rosemary, and bay leaf and season with pepper. Bring the mixture to a boil, then cover the casserole and transfer it to the oven. Cook the casserole for 1 ¼ hours.

5 Remove the lid of the pan and cook the casserole for another 30 minutes, stirring once or twice. Stir in the broad beans and cook, uncovered, for another 30 minutes, again stirring once or twice.

6 Taste and add pepper if necessary, and stir in the chopped parsley. If you are using the brandy, warm it in a small saucepan and pour it over the casserole. For added panache, immediately set the brandy on fire and carry the casserole to the table still flaming.

PER SERVING: 52 g protein, 21 g total fat, 6 g saturated fat, 94 mg cholesterol, 19 g carbohydrates, 9 g fibre.

Poultry

A real crowd-pleaser, versatile chicken has a light flavour that marries happily with just about any ingredients, from refreshing fruit to spicy sauces. These recipes are anything but dull, and they're sure to please everyone!

RICH CURRIED CHICKEN & VEGETABLES

SERVES 4

The homemade curry powder for this chicken dish has an especially high proportion of phytochemical-rich turmeric and ginger.

394 calories per serving

1 tbsp	turmeric	15 mL
1 ½ tsp	ground ginger	7 mL
¼ tsp	salt	1 mL
½ tsp	cinnamon	2 mL
½ tsp	sugar	2 mL
½ tsp	pepper	2 mL
1 ¼ pounds	skinless, boneless chicken thighs, cut into 1-inch (2.5-cm) chunks	500 g
2 tsp	olive oil	10 mL
	1 medium onion, halved and thickly sliced	
	4 cloves garlic, minced	
	3 carrots, thickly sliced	
1 pound	small red-skinned potatoes, quartered	450 g
2 tsp	creamy peanut butter	10 mL
	4 cups broccoli florets	

1 In a medium bowl, stir together the turmeric, ginger, ⅛ tsp (0.5 mL) of the salt, the cinnamon, sugar, and pepper. Add the chicken, tossing to coat.

2 In a nonstick Dutch oven, heat the oil over medium heat. Add the onion and garlic, and cook, stirring frequently for 7 minutes, or until the onion is tender.

3 Add ½ cup (125 mL) of water, the carrots, potatoes, peanut butter, and the remaining ⅛ teaspoon salt; bring to a boil. Cook for 5 minutes, or until the carrots begin to soften.

4 Add the chicken and cook for 2 minutes, or until no longer pink. Stir in 2 cups (500 mL) of water and bring to a boil. Reduce to a simmer; cover and cook for 15 minutes, or until the chicken is cooked through and the potatoes are tender.

5 Add the broccoli; cover and cook for 5 minutes, or until the broccoli is tender.

PER SERVING: 37 g protein, 10 g total fat, 2 g saturated fat, 118 mg cholesterol, 38 g carbohydrates, 8 g fibre.

Swap & Drop

hot-weather party

Put on your PARTY HAT

▶ Create a "Can't say no!" invite that gives a glimpse of the fun to come. Tape it to a paper umbrella or tie it to colourful plastic cutlery.

▶ "Shop" inside your home before breaking the bank. Decorate with oddball items—a bird-cage as centrepiece, baby carrots for bottle stoppers—that will be surefire conversation starters.

▶ Clear the decks before guests arrive; less stuff means more space to mingle.

▶ Pick up premade food to supplement your signature dish. Keep some energy for the party; it should be fun for you, too!

party! planner

Aloha!

Bring Hawaii home to your backyard or balcony with a quick trip to the dollar store to pick up some colourful grass skirts for your tables or railing.

for the kids
SMOOTHIE POPS

▶ Swap in plums, pears, or mango; they all blend up well.

▶ Blend together: 2 large peaches, 1 cup (250 mL) each of 1% yogurt and 1% milk. Pour into moulds and freeze for at least 2 hours.

Makes 6. Per pop: 76 calories, 4 g protein, 1 g fat, 1 g saturated fat, 4 mg cholesterol, 13 g carbohydrates, 2 g fibre.

Menu

Pesto-Stuffed Cherry Tomatoes (page 119) • *Kick things off with this fun-sized, digit-friendly one-bite popper.*

Roasted Chicken Salad with Ginger (page 164) • *An fresh, unexpected mix of summery flavours, delicious alone or served on a bed of cool, crunchy strips of lettuce.*

Blueberry-Strawberry Mousse (page 229). • *Your guests won't believe that this delectable dessert is just under 100 calories.*

Fun & Games

♣ Try your hand at croquet, horseshoes, sandbag toss, or bocce. Similar to lawn bowling, bocce involves a toss instead of a roll. All you need is 8 balls , a target, and a smallish patch of lawn to play on. This European game is addictively fun.

It may sound loco, but try dousing strawberries in balsamic vinegar, dusting them with sugar, and grating a dash of black pepper on top. This may be the oddest poolside snack you'll fall in love with.

LUSCIOUS & SLUSHY PUNCH

In a large pot, combine ½ cup (125 mL) SPLENDA® No Calorie Sweetener, Granulated, 6 cups (1.4 L) cold water, and 2 packages sugar-free raspberry gelatin. Boil 3 minutes, then stir in 1 can (46 ounces/1.4 L) pineapple juice, ⅔ cup (160 mL) lemon juice, and 1 quart (1 L) orange juice. Divide in 2 and freeze. When ready to serve, place the frozen contents of one container in a punch bowl and stir in 1 bottle (1 quart/1L) lemon-lime soft drink until slushy. Repeat, adding another bottle of lemon-lime soft drink, with second container. MAKES: 6 quarts/L PER SERVING (4 fluid ounces/120 mL): 60 calories

KUNG PAO CHICKEN

SERVES 4

The chicken is stir-fried instead of deep-fried, reducing the fat content in this healthier version of a popular dish. It is quite spicy, with the inclusion of dried red chili peppers, but you can also add a fresh long red chili pepper for additional kick!

1 pound	skinless chicken thighs, diced	500 g
2 tbsp	peanut oil, divided	30 mL
	2 cloves garlic, thinly sliced	
	8 dried red chili peppers, seeded and chopped	
1 tsp	crushed Szechuan peppercorns	5 mL
	2 green onions, sliced	
2 tbsp	salt-reduced soy sauce	30 mL
1 tbsp	shaoxing rice wine	15 mL
1 tsp	sugar	5 mL
⅓ cup	raw cashews or peanuts, toasted	50 g
	steamed rice, to serve	
	MARINADE	
2 tsp	salt-reduced soy sauce	10 mL
2 tsp	rice wine, or mirin	10 mL
1 tsp	sesame oil	5 mL
1 ½ tsp	cornstarch	7 mL

481 calories per serving

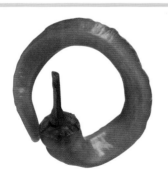

SWAP IT OUT!

● ● ● **Instead of chicken thighs,** you can add shrimp or scallops to this dish. You can also add any of your favourite vegetables, such as red pepper, green beans, sugarsnap peas, or snow peas.

1 To make the marinade, combine all of the ingredients in a shallow bowl. Add the chicken and toss to coat. Cover with plastic wrap and refrigerate for 30 minutes.

2 Heat 1 tbsp (15 mL) of the peanut oil in a wok or large non-stick frying pan over high heat. Add the chicken, in two batches if necessary, and cook for 5 minutes or until just golden. Remove to a plate.

3 Heat another 1 tbsp (15 mL) of the oil in the wok and add the garlic and stir-fry for 30 seconds. Add the chili peppers, Szechuan peppercorns, and the white part of the green onion and stir-fry for 1 minute, or until fragrant.

4 Combine the soy sauce, rice wine, and sugar in a small bowl, then add to the chili mixture in the wok and stir well. Add the chicken and stir-fry for about 2 minutes to heat through. Stir in the green onions and cashews. Remove from the heat, divide among serving bowls and serve with steamed rice.

PER SERVING: 36 g protein, 30 g fat, 8 g saturated fat, 70 mg cholesterol, 8 g carbohydrates, 2 g fibre.

**INGREDIENT
INTEL**
Szechuan peppercorns are a
little hotter than regular
black ones and have a
slightly lemony flavour. You
can also swap in any other
peppercorns that you
have on hand.

ROASTED CHICKEN SALAD WITH GINGER

Don't be tempted to omit fresh ginger—its subtle flavour makes all the difference!

355
calories per serving

3 ½ pound	broiler-fryer chicken, roasted, or	1.75-kg
1 ½ pounds	cooked boneless, skinless chicken breasts	750 g
3 tbsp	fresh lime juice	45 mL
	2 large green apples, unpeeled, cut in ½-inch (1-cm) pieces	
	4 celery stalks, thinly sliced	
1 cup	quartered, dried apricots	250 mL
1 cup	light sour cream	250 mL
½ cup	light mayonnaise	125 mL
1 tbsp	grated peeled ginger	15 mL
1 tsp	salt	5 mL
1 tsp	freshly ground black pepper	5 mL
¼ cup	minced white onion	60 mL
	GARNISH	
⅓ cup	toasted chopped walnuts	75 mL
	Sprigs of watercress	

1 If using a whole chicken, remove meat and discard skin and bones. Cut the chicken into bite-sized pieces and place in a large serving bowl.

2 Squeeze lime juice into a medium-sized bowl. Add apples and toss until well coated.

3 To the chicken, add the apples and any remaining lime juice, celery, and apricots. Toss gently until well mixed.

4 In a small bowl, stir together sour cream, mayonnaise, ginger, salt, and pepper. Fold in the onion. Spoon over the chicken mixture and toss gently until all the pieces are coated well. Sprinkle the toasted walnuts on top and garnish with sprigs of watercress.

PER SERVING: 35 g protein, 12 g total fat, 2 g saturated fat, 85 mg cholesterol, 30 g carbohydrates, 4 g fibre.

SWAP
Flavours

Chicken & grape salad: Add 1 cup (250 mL) red or purple seedless grapes, cut in half, with the apples, celery and apricots. Substitute ⅓ cup (75 mL) toasted slivered almonds for the walnuts.

Chicken & pineapple salad: Add 2 cups (500 mL) fresh pineapple wedges with the apples, celery and apricots.

Chicken & melon salad: Substitute 2 cups (500 mL) honeydew melon balls for the apricots.

SPICY DRUMSTICKS WITH CREOLE RICE

SERVES 4

These chicken drumsticks can be cooked under the broiler oron the grill in next to no time. Serve the them with steamed green vegetables and brown rice.

444 calories per serving

DRUMSTICKS		
1 tbsp	flour	15 mL
1 tsp	paprika	5 mL
1 tsp	ground black pepper	5 mL
1 tsp	garlic powder	5 mL
1 tsp	crushed red pepper	5 mL
1 tsp	dried thyme	5 mL
	8 chicken drumsticks, skinned	
1 tbsp	olive oil	15 mL
	Salt and pepper	
RICE		
1 tsp	olive oil	5 mL
	1 onion, chopped	
	1 red pepper, seeded and diced	
	2 celery stalks, diced	
1 cup	long-grain rice	250 mL
2 cups	low-sodium vegetable broth	500 mL
1 cup	canned red kidney beans, drained and rinsed	250 mL
2 tbsp	chopped parsley	30 mL
GARNISH		
	Sprigs of fresh parsley	

1 MORE IDEA

● ● ● **Sticky Chili Drumsticks with Bulgur**

Mix 2 tbsp (30 mL) low-sodium ketchup with 1 tbsp (15 mL) light soy sauce and 2 tbsp (30 mL) sweet chili sauce or paste. Rub onto the chicken drumsticks and grill as in the main recipe. Meanwhile, place 1 cup (250 mL) bulgur wheat in a heatproof bowl, pour over enough boiling water to cover, and soak for 15 to 20 minutes. Squeeze out any excess water, then mix with 1 cup (250 mL) canned red kidney beans, drained and rinsed; 1 small diced cucumber; 2 chopped tomatoes; 2 tbsp (30 mL) chopped fresh mint; and 2 tbsp (30 mL) chopped parsley. Add 1 tbsp (15 mL) lemon juice and 1 tbsp (15 mL) olive oil and season to taste. Toss to mix. Serve with the sticky chili drumsticks.

1 Preheat a grill to medium, or turn on oven broiler. Put the flour, paprika, pepper, garlic, red pepper, thyme, and a pinch of salt in a plastic zippered bag and shake to mix. Make 2 slashes in each chicken drumstick and rub with the olive oil. Toss them one at a time in the bag to coat with the spice mixture. Shake off any excess mixture and place the chicken on the grill or under the broiler. Cook until golden and cooked through, about 20 to 25 minutes, turning often.

2 Meanwhile, make the Creole rice. Heat the oil in a large saucepan, add the onion, pepper, and celery, and cook until softened, about 2 minutes. Stir in the rice, then add the broth and kidney beans. Bring to a boil. Cover and simmer gently until all the broth has been absorbed and the rice is tender, about 15 to 20 minutes.

3 Stir the chopped parsley into the rice, and season with salt and pepper to taste. Spoon the rice onto 4 plates and place 2 drumsticks on top of each portion. Serve hot, garnished with sprigs of parsley.

PER SERVING: 29 g protein, 10 g total fat, 2 g saturated fat, 69 mg cholesterol, 58 g carbohydrates, 6 g fibre.

SWAP & DROP

GOOD

369 calories

BETTER

283 calories

TURKEY & BLACK BEAN ENCHILADAS
SERVES 4

2 ½ cups/625 mL medium-hot salsa

¼ cup/60 mL chopped cilantro

1 tsp/5 mL ground cumin

8 6-inch/15-cm corn tortillas

8 ounces/250 g cooked turkey breast, shredded

¾ cup/175 mL canned black beans, rinsed and drained

1 small red onion, finely chopped

1 cup/250 mL shedded, light cheddar cheese

1 Preheat the oven to 350°F (180°C). Lightly spray a 7 x 11-inch (18 x 28-cm) baking dish with non-stick cooking spray.

2 Combine the salsa, cilantro, and cumin in a shallow bowl that is at least 6 inches (15 cm) in diameter. Working with one at a time, lay the tortillas flat in the salsa mixture, coating one side completely.

3 Place the tortillas, one at a time, on a plate or a sheet of wax paper. Top with 2 tbsp (25 mL) of the salsa mixture. Then again with ⅛ of the turkey, beans and red onion. Sprinkle with 1 tbsp (15 mL) cheese. Roll the tortillas up and place seam-side down in the baking dish. Repeat with the remaining tortillas.

4 Spoon the remaining salsa mixture over the enchiladas and sprinkle with the remaining ½ cup (125 mL) cheese. Bake until bubbling, about 15 minutes.

PER SERVING: 34 g protein, 7 g total fat, 3.5 g saturated fat, 62 mg cholesterol, 45 mg carbohydrates, 9 g fibre.

BALSAMIC-GLAZED TURKEY CUTLETS
SERVES 4

1 pound/450 g turkey cutlets

2 tbsp/30 mL flour

2 tbsp/30 mL olive oil

2 cups/ about 340 g cubed (½ inch/1 cm) butternut squash

2 tsp/10 mL sugar

¼ cup/60 mL balsamic vinegar

½ tsp/2 mL salt

½ tsp/2 mL sage

2 red apples (unpeeled), thinly sliced

1 tsp/10 mL cornstarch blended with 1 tbsp/15 mL water

1 Dredge the turkey in the flour, shaking off the excess. In a large non-stick frying pan, heat 1 tbsp (15 mL) of the oil over medium heat. Add half the turkey, and cook for 1 minute per side, or until golden brown and just cooked through. Transfer the turkey to a plate. Repeat with the remaining 1 tbsp (15 mL) oil and remaining turkey.

2 Add the squash to the pan, sprinkle with the sugar, and cook for 3 minutes, or until lightly browned. Add the vinegar, and cook for 1 minute.

3 Stir in 1 ¼ cups (310 mL) of water, the salt, and sage; bring to a boil. Reduce to a simmer and stir in the apples; cover and cook for 2 minutes, or until the squash and apples are tender.

4 Stir in the cornstarch mixture, and cook for 1 minute, or until lightly thickened. Return the turkey to the pan, and simmer gently for 1 minute, or until heated through.

PER SERVING: 29 g protein, 8 g total fat, 1 g saturated fat, 70 mg cholesterol, 25 g carbohydrates, 3 g fibre.

CHICKEN LEMONGRASS SKEWERS

These chicken lemongrass skewers make an impressive starter when entertaining and can be turned into a full meal served with steamed rice or a green salad.

1 ¼ pounds	ground chicken	600 g
1 tbsp	grated fresh ginger	15 mL
1 cup	chopped fresh cilantro leaves	30 g
1 long red chili pepper, seeded and chopped (optional)		
1 clove garlic, crushed		
2 tbsp	salt-reduced soy sauce	30 mL
1 tbsp	fresh lime juice	15 mL
4 stems lemongrass		
Canola oil spray, for cooking		
Lime wedges, to serve		
SOY GINGER DIPPING SAUCE (OPTIONAL)		
½ cup	salt-reduced soy sauce	125 mL
1 long red chili pepper, seeded and finely chopped		
3 tbsp	grated fresh ginger	45 mL
2 tbsp	rice vinegar	30 mL

257 calories per serving

Swap the flavour...

You can substitute the chicken with ground pork if you prefer.

▷ ...AND THE PRESENTATION

You can also take the meat off the skewers and wrap them in crisp lettuce leaves for a unique serving idea.

1 Combine the chicken, ginger, coriander, chili pepper, garlic, soy sauce, and lime juice in a bowl and use your hands to combine and coat the chicken.

2 To make the soy ginger dipping sauce, put all of the ingredients into a small bowl and stir well to combine. Trim the ends of each lemongrass stem and cut each in half lengthwise to make 8 skewers.

3 Divide the mixture into 8 even-sized portions. Shape one portion around the middle of each lemongrass skewer, moulding it with your hands to fit—this can be done ahead of time and refrigerated, covered, until you are ready to cook.

4 Preheat a grill pan or heat a barbecue to medium–high and spray the pan or grill rack with a little canola oil. Cook the skewers for 6 to 8 minutes, turning occasionally, until golden and cooked through. If desired, serve skewers with dipping sauce and lime wedges on the side.

PER SERVING: 30 g protein, 13 g total fat, 4 g saturated fat, 40 mg cholesterol, 5 g carbohydrate, 1 g fibre.

MEXICAN TOSTADAS

SERVES 8

A tostada is a flat, crisply fried corn tortilla with toppings. Here spicy tomato sauce and pinto beans replace the traditional refried beans.

329 calories per serving

1 ½ pounds	boneless, skinless chicken breasts	750 g
2 tbsp	canola oil	30 mL
	2 large red or green peppers, seeded and coarsely chopped	
	2 large yellow onions, chopped	
	2 large garlic cloves, thinly sliced	
1 tbsp	chili powder	15 mL
2 tsp	paprika	10 mL
1 tsp	ground cumin	5 mL
½ tsp	freshly ground black pepper	2 mL
¼ tsp	salt	1 mL
1 19-ounce can	low-salt chopped tomatoes	1 540-mL
½ tsp	sugar	2 mL
1 19-ounce can	pinto beans	1 540-mL can
8 6-inch	soft corn tortillas	8 15-cm
	TOPPINGS	
	2 large tomatoes, cut into 1-inch (2.5-cm) dice	
2 cups	shredded iceberg lettuce	500 mL
	4 pickled jalapeno peppers, coarsely chopped	
1 cup	shredded light cheddar cheese	250 mL
½ cup	low-fat sour cream	125 mL
	2 radishes, sliced	
	Bottled chunky tomato salsa	

SWAP
Flavours

Substitute 2 cups (500 mL) fresh or frozen corn kernels (cooked and drained) for the beans at end of Step 2.

1 Cook the chicken by simmering in an uncovered saucepan of water for about 20 minutes. Using a slotted spoon, transfer the chicken to a rack to cool. Shred the meat and set aside.

2 Heat 1 tbsp (15 mL) of the oil in a large frying pan over medium-high heat. Add the peppers, onions, and garlic. Sauté until softened, about 8 minutes. Stir in the chili powder, paprika, cumin, pepper, and salt; cook 2 minutes more. Stir in can of tomatoes and sugar. Simmer, uncovered, until the sauce thickens, about 8 minutes. Remove from heat and keep warm. Meanwhile, in a small saucepan, heat the beans over medium heat in their liquid; drain and rinse.

3 In a heavy frying pan (cast-iron, if you have one), heat remaining oil and toast tortillas, one at a time, over high heat, until slightly crisp and lightly browned, about 1 minute per side. Keep warm in foil.

4 To assemble, divide tomato sauce, beans, chicken, diced tomato, and lettuce among all 8 tostadas. Sprinkle with jalapenos. Top with 1 tbsp (15 mL) each of the cheddar cheese and sour cream, plus a radish slice and some salsa, if desired.

PER TOSTADA: 32 g protein, 8 g total fat, 1 g saturated fat, 67 mg cholesterol, 34 g carbohydrates, 8 g fibre.

RAW TRUTH
Certain foods are more nutritious cooked than raw. For intstance, the heating process increases the disease-fighting antioxidant of tomatoes.

fish & seafood

Fish and seafood can become your best diet buddies. They're packed with heart-healthy fats and protein, and seafood has a celebratory feel thanks to its delicate, rich flavours that help a little delicious seafood go a long way.

SEAFOOD JAMBALAYA

SERVES 4

A small amount of salmon and shrimp goes a long way in this one-bowl meal.

416 calories per serving

1 tbsp	olive oil	15 mL
	1 onion, chopped	
	2 celery stalks, sliced	
	1 green or red pepper, seeded and cut into strips	
	2 garlic cloves, crushed	
1 tsp	each, ground ginger, mild chili powder	5 mL
½ tsp	cayenne pepper	2 mL
1 cup	long-grain white rice	250 mL
2 cups	hot vegetable or reduced-sodium chicken broth	500 mL
1 14-ounce	can chopped tomatoes	1 398-mL
3 tbsp	coarsely chopped parsley	45 mL
½ lb	large raw shrimp, peeled and deveined	250 g
½ pound	skinned salmon fillet, cut into 1-inch (2.5-cm) cubes	250 g
	Salt, pepper, and a dash of hot red pepper sauce	

1 Heat oil in a deep, wide frying pan over medium heat. Add onion and cook, stirring, for 3 minutes. Add celery, pepper, garlic, ginger, cayenne, chili powder, and rice, and cook another 2 minutes.

2 Pour in the hot broth and stir well, then reduce the heat so that the broth is simmering gently. Cover the frying pan pan with a tight-fitting lid and simmer for 15 minutes.

3 Stir in the chopped tomatoes with their juice and 2 tbsp (30 mL) of the parsley, then add the shrimp and salmon. Cover again, and simmer until the seafood is just cooked and the rice has absorbed most of the liquid and is tender, about 3 to 4 minutes.

4 Add the hot sauce, if using, and season lightly with salt and pepper. Sprinkle with the remaining 1 tbsp (15 mL) parsley and serve hot.

PER SERVING: 30 g protein, 10 g total fat, 1 g saturated fat, 121 mg cholesterol, 50 g carbohydrates, 4 g fibre.

BAKED TROUT WITH CUCUMBER SAUCE

SERVES 4

Orange and lemon slices add a bright citrus flavour to this baked dish.

320
calories per serving

1 pound	new potatoes, quartered lengthwise	500 g
2 tsp	olive oil	10 mL
4 10-ounce	small trout, cleaned	4 300-g
	4 sprigs fresh tarragon	
	1 each, orange and lemon, cut into 8 slices	
4 tbsp	orange juice	60 mL
	SAUCE	
	1 large cucumber, peeled and seeded	
²/₃ cup	plain low-fat yogurt	150 mL
2 tbsp	chopped fresh mint	30 mL
	Salt and pepper	
	GARNISH	
1 cup	watercress	250 mL

1 Preheat the oven to 400°F (200°C) and put 2 baking sheets in the oven to heat. Carefully slip the potatoes intoa a pot of boiling water, then simmer for 5 minutes. Drain and return to the pot. Drizzle oil over potatoes and toss to coat. Spread them a hot baking sheet and roast for 10 minutes. Turn roast for another 10, then turn again and roast until crisp, about 5 minutes.

2 Meanwhile, tuck tarragon in the fish. Cut orange and lemon slices in half; divide half among 4 squares of foil large enough to wrap the fish pieces. Lay the fish on top; cover with remaining fruit slices. Sprinkle 1 tbsp (15 mL) orange juice over each fish. Enclose the fish in foil, twisting the ends to seal. Lay the parcels on the second hot baking sheet and bake for 20 minutes.

3 Grate the cucumber, then press out the water. Mix the cucumber, yogurt, and mint, and season lightly with salt and pepper. Arrange the fish, orange and lemon slices, and the roasted potatoes on warm plates. Add a garnish of watercress and serve with the cucumber sauce.

PER SERVING: 27 g protein, 9 g total fat, 2 g saturated fat, 65 mg cholesterol, 34 g carbohydrates, 4 g fibre.

SWAP Flavours

Vary the flavour of the sauce by adding 1 tsp (5 mL) prepared horseradish. Or, instead of mint, use 1 tbsp (15 mL) chopped fresh chives or green olives.

Mackerel can be substituted for the trout.

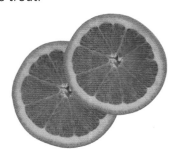

SWORDFISH WITH SALSA

Since the dressing can be made well in advance, this dish is ideal for entertaining. Serve with thin sesame breadsticks on the side.

280 calories per serving

SALSA		
1 large orange		
1 pound	tomatoes, seeded and diced	500 g
4 large green onions, green parts only, finely chopped		
1 each, orange and yellow bpepper, seeded and diced		
1 tsp	ground cumin, or to taste	5 mL
2 tsp	olive oil	10 mL
1 green chili pepper, seeded, and finely chopped		
Salt and pepper, to taste		
2 tbsp	finely chopped fresh cilantro	30 mL
4 5-ounce	swordfish steaks, ½-inch (1-cm) thick	4 150-g
1 tsp	olive oil	5 mL
2 cups	baby spinach leaves	500 mL
2 zucchini, coarsely grated		
1 tbsp	chopped parsley	15 mL

1 Prepare the salsa 20 minutes to 8 hours before serving. Grate zest from the orange and squeeze out 4 tbsp (60 mL) juice. Put both in a large mixing bowl and add tomatoes, onions, peppers, cumin, olive oil, and chili pepper. Season lightly, stir, cover, and refrigerate.

2 Turn on the oven broiler. Lightly brush swordfish steaks with some olive oil. Grill about 3 inches (7.5 cm) from the heat for 2 ½ minutes. Flip, brush with remaining oil, and broil until the edges are lightly charred and the flesh is just firm (about 2 to 3 minutes). Don't overcook or the swordfish will be tough and dry. Remove from the heat and set aside to cool slightly.

3 Meanwhile, put spinach leaves, zucchini, and parsley in a bowl and toss to mix. Divide among plates. Stir cilantro into the dressing. Break the swordfish into bite-sized pieces, add to the dressing, and gently mix in. Spoon dressed fish on top of the spinach salad and serve.

PER SERVING: 32 g protein, 10 g total fat, 0 g saturated fat, 54 mg cholesterol, 18 g carbohydrates, 5g fibre.

SWAP IT OUT!

● ● ● **Warm Mediterranean Tuna Salad**

Use 4 tuna steaks, 1 inch (2.5 cm) thick, about 5 ounces (150 g) each. Grill the steaks, basting with a mixture of 1 tsp (5 mL) extra-virgin olive oil and 1 tbsp (15 mL) orange juice, for 2 to 3 minutes on each side, according to how well done you like tuna. Instead of using the tomatoes in the salsa dressing, slice them. Make the salsa dressing omitting the cumin, chili pepper, and cilantro, and toss with 2 cups (500 mL) shredded radicchio and 1 cup (250 mL) arugula. Arrange the tomato slices and salsa salad on 4 plates, top with the tuna, broken into pieces, and scatter some shredded fresh basil over it.

SHRIMP PROVENÇAL

SERVES 4

The ideal pairing for this stylish main dish is a simple salad of sliced tomatoes.

369 calories per serving

1 tbsp	olive oil	15 mL
	1 large onion, chopped	
	1 bulb of fennel, chopped	
	1 large garlic clove, crushed	
1 19-ounce	can chopped tomatoes	1 540-mL
½ cup	reduced-sodium vegetable broth	125 mL
1 tbsp	fennel seeds	15 mL
	Finely grated zest and juice of 1 orange	
	Pinch of saffron threads	
1 cup	long-grain rice	250 mL
2 cups	water	500 mL
1 pound	large shrimp, peeled and deveined	500 g
	Salt and pepper	
	Fresh basil leaves, to garnish	

1 Heat oil in a large non-stick frying pan with a tight-fitting lid. Add onion, fennel, and garlic, and cook over medium heat, stirring occasionally, until softened, about 5 minutes. Add tomatoes, broth, fennel seeds, and orange zest and juice, and season lightly with salt and pepper. Bring to a boil, stirring, then reduce the heat to low and half-cover the pan. Simmer 12 minutes.

2 Meanwhile, crumble saffron threads into 2 cups (500 mL) water. Bring to a boil. Add the rice and simmer until tender, about 15 to 20 minutes.

3 Return tomato sauce to a boil. Add the shrimp on top, cover the pan tightly, and cook over low heat until the shrimp are cooked, about 3 to 4 minutes. Drain the rice and divide among serving bowls. Top with the shrimp and tomato sauce. Sprinkle with basil and serve at once.

PER SERVING: 26 g protein, 6 g total fat, 1 g saturated fat, 176 mg cholesterol, 54 g carbohydrates, 6 g fibre.

SWAP IT OUT!

● ● ● **Tuna Provençal**

Make the tomato sauce and, just before serving, stir in 1 can tuna packed in spring water, drained and flaked. This makes a great sauce for cooked pasta shells. Serve garnished with fresh dill.

● ● ● This combination of seafood and tomatoes also makes a delicious sauce on a bed of whole-wheat spaghetti.

● ● ● Use 2 chopped small zucchini instead of the fennel. Chopped green beans and red, yellow, orange, or green peppers also work well in the sauce.

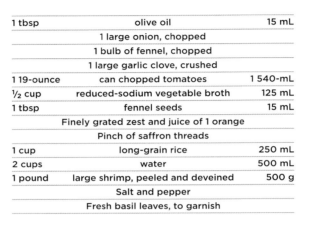

SWAP & DROP

487 *calories*

ITALIAN SEAFOOD STEW

SERVES 4

1 tbsp/15 mL olive oil

1 each, leek and onion chopped

4 garlic cloves, chopped

1 green pepper, seeded and chopped

1 medium bulb of fennel, diced

1 ½ cups/375 mL dry white wine

1 ¼ cups/300 mL light broth

1 28-ounce/796-mL can tomatoes

2 tbsp/30 mL tomato paste

1 tsp/5 mL dried herbes de Provence

1 zucchini, sliced

3 tbsp/45 mL chopped parsley

½ cup/125 mL each, peas, spinach/chard

½ pound/250 g skinless cod fillet, in chunks

1 pound/500 g mixed shellfish, unshelled

Polenta

1 Heat oil in a large saucepan, add leek and onion, and cook 2 minutes. Add garlic, pepper, and fennel, and cook 5 to 10 minutes, until soft.

2 Add wine, broth, and tomatoes. Simmer until the mixture has thickened slightly, about 30 minutes. Stir in tomato paste, herbes de Provence, and zucchini, and simmer for 10 minutes. Meanwhile, cook polenta according to package instructions, then pour into a shallow frying pan coated with cooking spray. Let cool; cut into triangles. Preheat a grill pan to high, or turn on the oven broiler.

3 Stir remaining vegetables, fish, and shellfish into the tomato mixture. Cover and simmer until seafood is just cooked, about 5 minutes. Lightly brush polenta triangles with oil and grill until lightly browned. Serve the fish stew in bowls with the polenta triangles.

PER SERVING: 39 g protein, 10 g total fat, 1 g saturated fat, 111 mg cholesterol, 58 g carbohydrates, 11 g fibre.

255 *calories*

SHRIMP GUMBO

SERVES 3

1 tbsp/15 mL olive oil

2 onions, chopped

1 red pepper, seeded and chopped

2 celery stalks, chopped

3 garlic cloves, chopped

2 slices turkey bacon, diced

1 tbsp/15 mL each, flour, paprika

3 cups/750 mL light broth

1 tsp/5 mL chopped fresh thyme

1 19-ounce /540-mL can chopped tomatoes

2 tbsp/30 mL chopped parsley

2 bay leaves

2 tsp/10 mL Worcestershire sauce

Hot sauce to taste

½ cup/125 mL okra, sliced crosswise

12 ounces/375 g shrimp, peeled and deveined

1 cup/250 mL green beans, cut in bite-sized pieces

Pepper, thinly sliced green onions (for garnish)

1 Heat oil in a large saucepan, add the onions, pepper, and celery and cook until lightly browned, 5 to 6 minutes. Stir in garlic and bacon and cook for 3 to 4 minutes. Add flour, increase the heat slightly, and cook for 2 minutes, stirring. Stir in paprika and cook for 2 more minutes. Gradually add broth, stirring well.

2 Add thyme, tomatoes, parsley, bay leaves, and Worcestershire sauce. Bring to a boil, then simmer and add hot sauce. Add okra and simmer until tender and gumbo has thickened, about 15 minutes.

3 Add shrimp and green beans, and cook until the shrimp turn pink, about 3 minutes. Remove bay leaves and season gumbo lightly with pepper. Serve in bowls, sprinkled with green onions.

PER SERVING: 27 g protein, 8 g total fat, 1 g saturated fat, 172 mg cholesterol, 21 g carbohydrates, 5 g fibre.

COD WITH SPICY LENTILS

SERVES 4

The texture of dark green puy lentils is a perfect complement to flaky fresh cod.

328 calories per serving

1 tbsp	olive oil, divided	15 mL
	1 onion, chopped	
	2 celery stalks, chopped	
	2 medium leeks, chopped	
	1 to 2 fresh red chili peppers, seeded and finely chopped	
1 cup	small lentils, rinsed and drained	250 mL
4 cups	reduced-sodium vegetable broth	1 L
	1 sprig fresh thyme	
	1 bay leaf	
	Juice of 1 lemon	
	Pinch of cayenne pepper	
4 4-ounce pieces	skinless cod fillets	4 125-g pieces
	or cod steaks	
	Salt and pepper, to taste	
	Lemon wedges, to serve	

1 Preheat grill pan to medium-high or turn on oven broiler. Heat half the olive oil in a saucepan, add onion, celery, leeks, and chili peppers; cook gently for 2 minutes. Stir in lentils. Add vegetable broth, thyme, and bay leaf, and bring to a boil. Lower the heat and simmer until lentils are tender, about 20 minutes. If the lentils have not absorbed all the broth, drain them.

2 Mix together the remaining oil, lemon juice, and cayenne pepper. Lay the cod on a grill pan or broiler pan, season lightly with salt and pepper, and brush with the oil mixture. Grill or oven-broil until the fish flakes easily, about 6 to 7 minutes. There is no need to turn the fish.

3 Spread lentils on a warmed serving dish and arrange cod on top. Serve with lemon wedges.

PER SERVING: 33 g protein, 5 g total fat, 0 g saturated fat, 50 mg cholesterol, 38 g carbohydrates, 12 g fibre.

SHOPPING

Sustainable ingredients

Pacific cod is on David Suzuki's Top 10 list of sustainable seafoods, along with closed-containment farmed salmon, which is a good substitute for the cod in this dish. The other seafood that makes Suzuki's list are farmed oyster and clams, swordfish, sardines, albacore tuna, sablefish, Dungeness crab, and spot prawns.

HONEY & MUSTARD SALMON

SERVES 4

Butter beans are a type of lima; any lima you prefer can be swapped in!

410 calories per serving

1 tbsp	canola oil	15 mL
1 tbsp	soy sauce	15 mL
2 tsp	honey	10 mL
2 tsp	whole-grain mustard	10 mL
	Grated zest and juice of 1 lemon	
4 4-ounce	skinless salmon fillets	4 125-g
2 14-ounce	cans butter beans, drained and rinsed	2 398-mL
	1 large garlic clove, crushed	
2 tbsp	extra virgin olive oil	30 mL
	Pinch of crushed chili flakes	
7 ounces	fresh baby leaf spinach, rinsed	200 g
	12 vine-ripened cherry tomatoes	

1 Mix the vegetable oil, soy sauce, honey, mustard, and 1 tbsp (15 mL) of lemon juice. Add salmon and coat with marinade. Set aside.

2 Put the beans and garlic in a pan with olive oil, remaining lemon juice, zest, and chili flakes.

3 Heat a grill pan or frying pan. Meanwhile, tip the spinach into a dry pan with only the water that clings to its leaves and stir over low heat for 2 minutes or until wilted. Drain and set aside. Gently heat the beans; set aside.

4 Cook the salmon in the heated ridged griddle or frying pan for 2 to 3 minutes on each side or until just firm and pink. Add the tomatoes for the last 1 to 2 minutes of the cooking time.

5 Roughly crush the beans with a vegetable masher or fork. Stir in the spinach and seasoning. Divide the beans and spinach among four serving plates. Arrange a salmon fillet on top of each and scatter the tomatoes around the side. Serve at once.

PER SERVING: 32 g protein, 22 g total fat, 3.5 g saturated fat, 92 mg cholesterol, 21 g carbohydrates, 11 fibre.

SWAP IT OUT!

● ● ● **Baked Salmon & Avocado Salsa**

Preheat the oven to 425°F (220°C). Prepare the salmon and its marinade in a shallow ovenproof dish. Bake the salmon, uncovered, for 15 minutes or until it flakes easily and is browned in places. For the salsa, halve, pit and dice 2 avocados. Add 2 tbsp (30 mL) white wine vinegar, 2 tbsp (30 mL) chopped candied ginger, and 1 crushed garlic clove. Snip 4 scallions and the tender ends and leaves from 1 ounce (30 g) fresh cilantro over the salsa. Mix lightly. Serve the salmon with the beans and spinach for the main recipe, with the salsa instead of the tomatoes.

5 shrimps
Each of these has 24 calories,
0 g fat, and 35 mg cholesterol.

OCEAN TREATS

Seafood is generally low in fat and calories. And, according to Agriculture Canada, eating more seafood is associated with a decreased risk of cardiovascular death. Here, shown in actual size, are seven different types of shellfish and seafood.

1 lobster claw
The meat of this claw has 37 calories, 0 g fat, and 40 mg cholesterol.

3 P.E.I. oysters
Each of these has 8 calories, 0.2 g fat, and 7 mg cholesterol.

7 mussels
Each of these has 9 calories,
0 g fat, and 3 mg cholesterol.

3 sea scallops
Each of these has 31 calories,
0 g fat, and 15 mg cholesterol.

8 sticks imitation crab
Real crab is best, but it can be
pricey. This is made of a variety
of fish meat and has added
ingredients including sodium.
Each of these pieces has 24
calories, 0.5 g fat, and 2 mg
cholesterol.

6 clams
Each of these has 7 calories,
0 g fat, and 3 mg cholesterol.

TUNA & ARTICHOKE STROGANOFF SERVES 4

This casserole is fast, easy, and delicious: a winning weeknight combination for the busy home cook.

430 calories per serving

16 ounces	frozen chopped spinach	500 g
½ cup	whole-wheat bread crumbs	125 mL
	1 large yellow pepper, chopped	
1 14-ounce	can artichoke hearts, chopped	1 398-mL
1 cup	fat-free sour cream	250 mL
⅔ cup	shredded low-fat cheddar cheese	150 mL
2 6-ounce	cans low-sodium tuna	2 172- g
½ 12-ounce	package of broad egg noodles	½ 340-g

1 Preheat oven to 400°F. Bring a pot of water to a boil and cook egg noodles according to package directions, adding yellow pepper for the last 30 seconds of cooking. Meanwhile, combine bread crumbs and cheese in a bowl.

2 Drain noodles and peppers, and return to pot. Stir in tuna, sour cream, spinach, and artichoke hearts. Pour into a medium-sized casserole dish, and sprinkle bread crumb mixture evenly over top.

3 Bake for 15 minutes or until golden on top and heated through. Divide among 4 serving plates, and garnish with reserved pieces of yellow pepper.

PER SERVING: 39 g protein, 7 g total fat, 2 g saturated fat, 81 mg cholesterol, 54 g carbohydrates, 7 g fibre.

:) TIME SAVER

Wash baby spinach in a colander, then cook it by pouring boiling water over it in the sink and leaving it to wilt. It only takes a few minutes and there's no pan to wash up.

COCONUT CURRY COD WITH BOK CHOY

SERVES 4

You can use either fresh or frozen fillets for this recipe.

2 tbsp	extra virgin olive oil	30 mL
1 tbsp each	minced garlic, grated ginger, curry powder	15 mL
	4 green onions, thinly sliced	
1 cup	canned light coconut milk	250 mL
1 cup	low-sodium chicken stock	250 mL
2 tbsp	lime juice	30 mL
	16 cilantro leaves	
4 4-ounce	cod fillets	4 120-g
	Salt and pepper	
	4 heads baby bok choy, rinsed	
	¼ each, red and yellow pepper, julienned	
	2 green onion tops, julienned	
½ cup	bean sprouts, rinsed	125 mL

423 calories per serving

SWAP
Flavours

The coconut curry sauce is also great with **MUSSELS**; prepare in a heavy-bottomed pot, and steam them until they open.

1 To a saucepan over medium heat, add olive oil, garlic, ginger, curry powder, and green onions, and sauté until onions soften. Add coconut milk, chicken stock, lime juice and cilantro (reserve a few leaves); turn heat to low and simmer for two minutes.

2 Add cod and cook, covered, for 8 to 10 minutes, or until done. Season with salt and pepper.

3 While fish cooks, place bok choy in a small pan with ½ cup (125 mL) of water and cook, covered, for 4 minutes. In a small bowl, place peppers, green onion tops, bean sprouts, and reserved cilantro leaves; toss to combine.

4 Divide coconut curry sauce among 4 plates. Place a piece of fish and bok choy on each. Garnish with julienned vegetable mixture.

PER SERVING: 36 g protein, 23 g total fat, 12 g saturated fat, 73 mg cholesterol, 28 g carbohydrates, 10 g fibre.

SEAFOOD WITH WATERCRESS DRESSING

SERVES 4

These poached scallops and salmon fillet are perfect with warm crusty bread.

½ pound	skinless salmon fillet, cut in 4 strips	250 g
½ pound	bay scallops	250 g
3 tbsp	dry white wine	45 mL
1 cup	fish stock or bottled clam juice	250 mL
	Thin slice of fresh ginger, unpeeled	
½ pound	sugar snap peas	250 g
	8 radishes	
4 cups	mixed salad leaves	1 L
	DRESSING	
1 ½ cups	watercress, chopped	375 mL
	1 shallot, chopped	
	Thin strip of lemon zest	
2 tbsp	snipped fresh chives	30 mL
1 tsp	lemon juice	5 mL
2 tbsp	plain low-fat yogurt	30 mL
	Salt and pepper	

188 calories per serving

1 Place the salmon into a non-aluminum saucepan or sauté pan with a tight-fitting lid—the pan should be just big enough for the salmon to fit in one layer. Arrange scallops on top. Pour in the wine and fish stock, then add ginger. Bring to a boil over a medium heat, then lower the heat until the liquid is simmering very gently. Cover and poach until the salmon and scallops are cooked and feel just firm to the touch, about 5 to 8 minutes.

2 Meanwhile, drop peas into a pan of boiling water and cook until just tender-crunchy, about 3 to 4 minutes. Drain, refresh under cold running water, then set aside. Slice the radishes or make radish flowers. Put the mixed salad leaves into a bowl. Add peas and radishes and mix well.

3 With a slotted spoon, lift seafood out of the pan onto a plate. Reserve the poaching liquid. Cut each strip of salmon in half, or flake into large chunks. Arrange the salmon and scallops on top of the salad.

4 To make the dressing, remove the tough stalks from the watercress and reserve. Drop the leaves into a pan of boiling water and bring back to a boil. Immediately drain and refresh under cold running water. Squeeze out excess water, then chop very finely.

5 Put the reserved watercress stalks in a pan with shallot, lemon zest, and 1/2 cup (125 mL) poaching liquid. Half-cover the pan and simmer 5 minutes. Strain, discarding the zest and vegetables. Stir in the chopped watercress, chives, lemon juice, and yogurt, and season with salt and pepper. Spoon the warm dressing over the salad and serve.

PER SERVING: 22 g protein, 7 g total fat, 1 g saturated fat, 50 mg cholesterol, 9 g carbohydrates, 2 g fibre.

TO MAKE RADISH FLOWERS

Cut 5 slits on each radish, cutting down from the top almost to the base. Put into a bowl of iced water and leave until the "petals" open slightly.

PARMESAN-TOPPED MUSSELS

Make this dish when you can buy large mussels.

190 calories per serving

½ cup	white wine or low-sodium vegetable broth	125 mL
	1 large onion, very finely chopped	
	3 large garlic cloves, crushed	
	About 30 large mussels, scrubbed, with beards removed	
	1 slice fresh whole-grain bread	
¼ cup	each, chopped parsley, grated Parmesan	60 mL
1 tbsp	finely grated lemon zest	15 mL
	Pinch of cayenne pepper	
2 tsp	olive oil	10 mL
	Lemon wedges, to garnish	

1 Pour wine or broth into a large saucepan, add onion and garlic, and bring to a boil over high heat. Boil rapidly for 1 minute. Add mussels, cover the pan tightly and cook for 2 to 3 minutes, shaking the pan occasionally. Uncover and give the mussels a good stir. Using tongs, remove them from the pan as soon as they open; set aside. Discard any mussels that remain shut.

2 When cool enough to handle, remove and discard the top shell. Place mussels on the half shell in a single layer in a shallow flameproof dish, loosening the mussels from the shells but leaving them in place.

3 Preheat an oven broiler. Put the bread in a food processor or blender and process to fine crumbs. Add the parsley, Parmesan, lemon zest, cayenne pepper, and olive oil, and process again until well blended.

4 Use your fingers to mound the cheese and crumb mixture on each mussel, packing it firmly so the mussel is covered. Broil until the crumb topping is crisp and lightly browned, about 2 to 3 minutes. Divide the mussels among individual plates and serve with lemon wedges.

PER SERVING: 19 g protein, 8 g total fat, 2 g saturated fat, 41 mg cholesterol, 12 g carbohydrates, 1 g fibre.

INGREDIENT INTEL
Mussels are available year-round, but get used less frequently than clams and oysters. They have a delightfully sweet flavour. Buy a few extra for any recipe, as some might remain unopened and have to be discarded.

SHRIMP WITH PEPPER SALSA

Serve these kebabs with brown rice or a piece of crusty bread.

32 large shrimp, peeled, deveined, tails left on		
1 cantaloupe, seeded and cut into 2-inch (5-cm) cubes		
MARINADE		
2 tbsp	lime juice	30 mL
1 tsp	each, chopped garlic and ginger	5 mL
SALSA		
6 medium tomatoes, chopped		
1 small red onion, finely chopped		
1 red pepper, seeded and chopped		
1 tsp	chopped garlic	5 mL
1 green chili pepper, seeded and finely chopped		
2 tbsp	lime juice	30 mL
2 tbsp	chopped fresh cilantro	30 mL
Salt and pepper, to taste		
Chopped green onions, to garnish		

86 calories per serving

INGREDIENT INTEL

Called **scampi** in Italy, but known in North America as shrimp, this crustacean is a rich source of protein and B vitamins.

The vitamin C in **tomatoes** is concentrated in the jelly-like substance surrounding the seeds. Vitamin C is an important nutrient for maintaining immunity and healthy skin.

Fennel seeds are thought to aid digestion, and fennel tea is often recommended to ease flatulence.

1 Soak 8 bamboo skewers in cold water for 30 minutes. Combine ingredients for the marinade in a shallow dish. Add the shrimp and stir to coat. Cover and set aside in the fridge.

2 Mix salsa ingredients; season with salt and pepper. Pile into a serving bowl. Thread melon cubes onto 8 unsoaked wooden skewers and place on a serving dish. Set aside.

3 Thread 4 shrimp onto each soaked skewer, piercing them through both ends. Grill until they are pink, about 3 to 4 minutes, turning them once. Garnish the salsa with the green onions. Place shrimp kebabs on a serving dish with melon and serve at once, with the salsa alongside.

PER SERVING: 7 g protein, 1 g total fat, 0 g saturated fat, 47 mg cholesterol, 15 g carbohydrates, 3 g fibre.

Meatless & sides

The latest research says you no longer have to consume starch and legumes (such as rice and beans) at the same meal to benefit from their protein. Pair legumes with a food source of vitamin C to help boost iron absorption. Some good news? Vegetarians tend to absorb and retain more calcium than meat-eaters, are at reduced risk for heart disease, and have lower rates of high blood pressure and diabetes.

BROILED MARINATED TOFU

SERVES 4

These marinated tofu "steaks" can be served hot, cold, or at room temperature. Serve 4 triangles as a main course (perhaps on a bed of shredded spinach), or serve 2 to 3 as a first course or as part of a buffet. If you can find pressed tofu, skip step 1.

2 19-ounce	blocks firm tofu	2 540-g
¼ cup	reduced-sodium soy sauce	60 mL
2 tbsp	fresh lemon juice	30 mL
4 tsp	dark brown sugar	20 mL
2 tsp	dark sesame oil	10 mL
4 tsp	sesame seeds	20 mL
	4 green onions, thinly sliced	

461
calories per serving

1 Slice each block of tofu in half horizontally. Lay the 4 pieces of tofu on a cutting board and place a can or small bowl under one end of the board to tilt it slightly. Set the board so that the low end hangs over the sink. Cover the tofu with paper towels, place another cutting board on top and weight it with a heavy pan or a couple of cans. Let drain for 2 hours.

2 In a shallow container (like a gratin dish or lasagna pan) large enough to hold the tofu in a single layer, whisk together the soy sauce, lemon juice, brown sugar, and sesame oil. Place the pressed tofu in the pan and let stand for 3 hours, or until the marinade has been absorbed about halfway up the tofu (there should still be some marinade in the container).

3 Turn on the broiler. Remove the tofu from the marinade, reserving any leftover. Place the tofu on a broiler pan, and broil 6 inches (15 cm) from the heat for 5 minutes per side, or until richly browned.

4 Meanwhile, in a small skillet, toast the sesame seeds over low heat for 3 minutes, or until golden.

5 To serve, cut each piece of tofu into 4 triangles and sprinkle with the green onions, sesame seeds, and any leftover marinade.

PER SERVING: 44 g protein, 27 g total fat, 4 g saturated fat, 0 mg cholesterol, 20 g carbohydrates, 1 g fibre.

LENTIL-TOMATO STEW WITH BROWNED ONIONS SERVES 4

This hearty vegetarian main course is rich in dietary fibre and beta-carotene. Non-vegans might want to serve the soup topped with crumbled goat cheese.

290 calories per serving

INGREDIENT INTEL
Eating **shiitake mushrooms** may enhance immunity. Researchers believe, the healing compounds they contain, including lentinan, may stimulate the body's production of immune cells.

1 cup	dried shiitake mushrooms	80 g
1 cup	boiling water	250 mL
4 tsp	olive oil	60 mL
	3 carrots, diced	
	8 cloves garlic, thinly sliced	
1 cup	lentils, rinsed and picked over	200 g
1 cup	canned crushed tomatoes	200 g
1 tsp	each, salt, ground cumin, ground ginger, sage	5 mL
	1 large onion, halved and thinly sliced	
2 tsp	sugar	10 mL
1 cup	frozen peas	250 mL

1 In a small bowl, combine the shiitake mushrooms and boiling water. Let stand for 20 minutes, or until softened. With your fingers, remove the mushrooms from the soaking liquid, reserving the liquid. Trim any stems from the mushrooms and thinly slice the caps. Strain the reserved liquid through a fine-meshed sieve or coffee filter; set aside.

2 In a large saucepan, heat 3 tsp (15 mL) of the oil over medium heat. Add the carrots and garlic, and cook for 5 minutes, or until softened.

3 Stir in the lentils, tomatoes, salt, cumin, ginger, sage, mushrooms, and reserved liquid. Add 3 cups (750 mL) of water, and bring to a boil. Reduce to a simmer; cover and cook for 35 minutes, or until the lentils are tender.

4 Meanwhile, in a large frying pan, heat the remaining 1 tsp (5 mL) oil over medium heat. Add the onion and sugar; cook, stirring frequently for 5 minutes, or until the onion is lightly browned.

5 Add the peas to the stew, and cook for 2 minutes to heat through. Serve the stew topped with the browned onions.

PER SERVING: 15 g protein, 5.5 g total fat, 0.7 g saturated fat, 0 mg cholesterol, 49 g carbohydrates, 10 g fibre.

PENNE RIGATI WITH SESAME-ORANGE DRESSING SERVES 4

This pasta salad is wonderful on its own or as a side dish with grilled chicken or firm fish. Any type of pasta can be used in this recipe, including rice noodles or orzo.

8 ounce	penne noodles	250 g
	2 large oranges	
	6 green onions, cut into short fine strips	
½ cup	bean sprouts (optional)	125 mL
2 tbsp	sesame seeds, toasted	30 mL
	DRESSING	
	Grated zest and juice of 1 orange	
1 tbsp	dark sesame oil	15 mL
2 tbsp	light soy sauce	30 mL
	1 garlic clove, crushed	
1 tbsp	finely grated peeled fresh ginger	15 mL
	Salt and pepper	

334 calories per serving

SWAP UP
Nutrients

Use Japanese soba noodles (made from buckwheat flour) instead of penne, and cook them for 5 to 7 minutes.

1 Cook the pasta in boiling water for 10 to 12 minutes, until al dente.

2 Meanwhile, peel oranges, removing pith. Holding oranges over a bowl to catch any juice, cut out segments from their membrane. Set the segments aside, and reserve the juice in the bowl.

3 Place the green onion strips in a bowl of cold water and set them aside until they curl.

4 Make the dressing: Add orange zest and to the reserved juice. Add the sesame oil, soy sauce, garlic, grated fresh ginger, and salt and pepper to taste. Whisk lightly to mix. Drain the pasta and add to the dressing. Mix well, then cover and set aside to cool.

5 When ready to serve, drain the green onions; reserve a few for garnish and add the remainder to the salad together with the orange segments, bean sprouts (if using) and toasted sesame seeds. Gently toss salad, then serve it at once, sprinkled with the reserved green onions.

PER SERVING: 12 g protein, 7 g total fat, 1 g saturated fat, 0 mg cholesterol, 58 g carbohydrates, 6 g fibre.

INGREDIENT INTEL

Oranges contain coumarins, compounds that are believed to help thin the blood and thus prevent stroke and heart attacks.

GREEK STUFFED GRAPE LEAVES

SERVES 8

Here's a new, healthy twist on these delicious and popular little Greek parcels. To boost the fibre and nutrient content, brown rice is used instead of the traditional white rice. The filling for the grape leaves is flavoured with garlic and fresh herbs, with a hint of sweetness from the raisins and crunch from the walnuts.

165
calories per trio

	GRAPE LEAVES	
1 cup	long-grain brown rice	250 mL
	24 large grape leaves preserved in brine, drained	
2 tsp	olive oil, divided	10 mL
	1 onion, finely chopped	
	1 large garlic clove, finely chopped	
1 tbsp	chopped parsley	15 mL
1 tbsp	chopped fresh mint	15 mL
1 tbsp	chopped fresh dill	15 mL
	Grated zest and juice of 1 lemon	
½ cup	raisins	125 mL
¼ cup	chopped walnuts	60 mL
	Salt and pepper	
	GARNISH	
	Lemon wedges	
	Sprigs of fresh dill, parsley, or mint	

AROMATIC EDIBLE
Toasting **raw nuts** before adding them to a dish helps to make the nuts more flavourful and aromatic.

1 Bring 2 cups (500 mL) of water to a boil. Add the rice and return to a boil. Lower the heat, cover and simmer until rice is tender, about 40 minutes. Remove from heat.

2 While the rice is cooking, drain the grape leaves, rinse with cold water and pat dry with a paper towel.

3 Heat 1 tsp (5 mL) of the oil in a saucepan over medium heat. Add the onion and garlic, and cook until soft but not browned, stirring occasionally, for 5 to 8 minutes. Remove from the heat and stir in the parsley, mint, dill, lemon zest, and raisins.

4 Place the walnuts in a small frying pan and toast them over medium heat until lightly browned and fragrant, stirring constantly. Add the toasted walnuts to the onion mixture. Stir in the cooked rice and add the lemon juice (you may not need all of it), and season lightly with salt and pepper. Mix well.

5 Spread one of the grape leaves flat on a work surface and place about 2 spoonfuls of the rice mixture into the centre. Fold over the stalk end, then fold in the sides. Roll up the leaf into the shape of a cylinder. Repeat with the remaining grape leaves and filling.

6 Place the rolls seam side down in a steamer and brush the tops with the remaining 1 tsp (5 mL) of oil. Cover and steam until piping hot, about 10 to 15 minutes. Serve hot or at room temperature, garnished with lemon wedges and sprigs of fresh herbs.

PER SERVING: 3 g protein, 4 g total fat, 0 g saturated fat, 0 mg cholesterol, 29 g carbohydrates, 2 g fibre.

**RINSE TO
REMOVE THE SALT**
When using grape leaves
that are preserved in brine,
always rinse them
thoroughly first, as brine is
extremely high in salt.

MUSHROOM RAVIOLI IN HERB JUS

SERVES 6

This is not a convenience meal, but it is well worth the time it takes! If you want to make everything from scratch, pull out the pasta-maker, but you can save yourself the effort by buying fresh lasagna strips from the supermarket and rolling them out a little thinner.

643 calories per serving

SHOPPING

Easy peasy

Store-bought wonton wrappers can be used instead of pasta to make ravioli.

	Fresh lasagna noodles, or homemade pasta	
	RAVIOLI FILLING	
4 tbsp	extra virgin olive oil	60 mL
	4 shallots, chopped	
	1 garlic clove, chopped	
¾ pound	mushrooms, finely chopped	450 g
4 tbsp	brandy	60 mL
	pepper to taste	
1 ounce	dried porcini mushrooms, soaked, drained and finely chopped	30 g
1 ¼ cups	fresh whole-wheat breadcrumbs	300 mL
1 ½ ounces	Parmesan cheese, freshly grated	50 g
	2 eggs	
2 tbsp	chopped fresh parsley or basil	30 mL
1 tsp	chopped fresh marjoram or ¼ tsp/1 mL dried marjoram	5 mL
	Fresh lasagna noodles	
1 ½ cups	snow peas or sugar snap peas	250 g
2 tbsp	tiny tender sprigs fresh thyme, to garnish	30 mL
1 tbsp	extra virgin olive oil to serve (optional)	15 mL
	HERB JUS	
3 cups	reduced-salt chicken or vegetable stock	750 mL
¾ cup	dry white wine	200 mL
	1 garlic clove, chopped	
1 tbsp	fresh thyme leaves or	15 mL
¼ tsp	dried thyme	1 mL
	4 zucchini, thinly sliced or coarsely diced	

1 Heat the olive oil in a large saucepan. Add the shallots and cook for a few seconds, then add the garlic and the mushrooms. Cook over high heat, stirring, to brown the mushrooms, then reduce the heat and cook for 10 minutes or until the mixture has reduced in volume.

2 Pour in brandy and cook, stirring, until it has evaporated. Remove from heat and add pepper.

3 Stir in the porcini mushrooms, breadcrumbs, Parmesan cheese, eggs, parsley, and marjoram. The ingredients should form a moist paste. Place in the fridge while you prepare the pasta.

4 Lightly roll strips of lasagna noodes. Lay a strip on the work surface. Dot the filling on the dough in small mounds (about 1 tsp/5 mL each), about 2 inches (5 cm) apart. Ensure that there is enough room between the mounds of filling for the covering of dough to stick to the base. Brush the dough around each mound with a little water. Top with a second strip of pasta and press it down firmly around the filling to seal. Cut between the mounds of filling with a fluted pastry wheel or sharp knife.

5 Carefully pull the ravioli apart and toss with the flour. Place in a single layer on a plate in the fridge. Repeat with the remaining dough and filling.

6 To make the herb jus, combine the stock, wine, and garlic in a saucepan. Bring to a boil and cook over high heat for 5 to 10 minutes or until the liquid is well flavoured. Add the thyme and zucchini, and continue cooking over medium-high heat for 5 to 10 minutes, or until the zucchini is tender but not mushy, and the liquid has intensified in flavour and evaporated slightly.

7 Meanwhile, cook the ravioli in boiling water for 4 to 5 minutes or until they rise to the surface. Add the snow or sugar snap peas for the final 30 to 60 seconds of cooking. Drain well.

8 Serve the ravioli and snow peas in shallow soup bowls with the herb jus ladled over. Sprinkle thyme over the top and drizzle with the 1 tbsp/15 mL olive oil, if using. Serve at once.

PER SERVING: 28 g protein, 25 g total fat, 6 g saturated fat, 224 mg cholesterol, 70 g total carbohydrates, 8 g fibre.

INGREDIENT INTEL
Mushrooms are low in fat and calories, and they also provide useful amounts of copper as well as some of the B vitamins.

NOODLE-STUFFED THAI OMELETTES

SERVES 4

For these delectable chili-flavoured omelettes, the eggs are whisked with cornstarch to give them a slightly firmer texture, suitable for folding around a tasty filling.

4 ounces	rice vermicelli	125 g
1 tbsp	cornstarch	15 mL
	8 eggs	
¼–½ tsp	crushed dried red chili peppers	1-2 mL
2 tbsp	canola oil	30 mL
1 tsp	sesame oil	5 mL
1 ¼ cups	sliced button or Swiss brown mushrooms	375 mL
	2 carrots, cut into thin matchsticks	
	1 green pepper, halved, seeded, and thinly sliced	
2 ¼ cups	shredded cabbage	560 mL
2 tbsp	salt-reduced soy sauce	30 mL
2 tsp	white wine vinegar	10 mL
2 tsp	grated fresh ginger	10 mL
	GARNISH	
1 tbsp	sesame seeds (optional)	15 mL

380 calories per serving

1 Put the cornstarch in a large bowl with ¼ cup (60 mL) water and mix well until smooth. Add the eggs and whisk together until well combined. Stir in the chili pepper and season with a little black pepper.

2 Heat 1 tsp (5 mL) of the canola oil in an 8-inch (20-cm) non-stick frying pan over medium heat. Pour in one quarter of the egg mixture, tipping the pan to spread out the egg in a thin, even layer. Cook for 2 minutes, or until set and golden. Remove to a plate and keep warm. Repeat with more oil and egg to make 4 omelettes in total.

3 Heat the remaining canola oil with the sesame oil in a wok or large non-stick frying pan. Add the mushrooms, carrots, green pepper, and cabbage and stir-fry for 4 to 5 minutes, or until the vegetables are just tender. Add the soy sauce, vinegar, ginger, and noodles. Gently toss until heated through.

4 Divide the vegetable and noodle mixture among the omelettes and fold them in half. Sprinkle with the sesame seeds, if using, and serve at once.

PER SERVING: 17 g protein, 20 g total fat, 4 g saturated fat, 106 mg cholesterol, 32 g carbohydrate, 4 g fibre,

SHOPPING

Rice noodle primer

Rice noodles come in various sizes, sold dry and wok-ready. Vermicelli noodles are very thin, rice stick noodles are thicker, and fine rice noodles are in between. All need to be soaked in hot water to soften before using. Microwave, steam, or submerge them briefly in warm water to separate them. Add at the end of cooking.

STEAMED VEGETABLES WITH PEANUT DIP

This easy-to-make party favourite is rich in fibre and bursting with flavour.

136 calories per serving

²/₃ cup	water	160 mL
¹/₃ cup	smooth peanut butter	80 mL
	1 clove garlic, minced	
2 tsp	grated fresh ginger	10 mL
	2 green onions, chopped	
2 tbsp	brown sugar	30 mL
2 tbsp	soy sauce	30 mL
	Pinch of chili powder	
1 tbsp	freshly squeezed lemon juice	15 mL
	6 large carrots, peeled, halved lengthways, cut in sticks, or 16 baby carrots with tops	
	2 large red or yellow peppers, halved and seeded, sliced ¼ inch (5 mm) thick	
½ pound	snow peas or green beans, trimmed	250 g
	8 radishes, thinly sliced	

1 Bring water to a boil in a small pot. Stir in peanut butter, garlic, ginger, green onion, sugar, soy sauce, and chili powder. Simmer 2 minutes; remove from heat. Stir in lemon juice; set aside.

2 In a large pot with a steamer basket, bring water to a boil. Fill a bowl with ice water. Steam carrots for 3 minutes, lift out and plunge into ice water to cool. Do the same for pepper (steam 1 minute) and snow peas or beans (2 minutes). Drain vegetables and dry with paper towels.

3 Spoon peanut dip into a small bowl and place on a serving platter. Arrange the carrot sticks, pepper, snow peas, or green beans around the bowl. Add radish as a garnish.

PER SERVING: 5 g protein, 6 g total fat, 1 g saturated fat, 0 mg cholesterol, 19 g carbohydrates, 5 g fibre.

STORAGE TIP

If you like the sharp taste of raw endives, don't wash them until they're ready to use, or they'll get mushy. Avoid exposure to light to preserve flavour; remove the bitter bottom core befor eating. the whiter the endive, the milder the taste.

196

ROASTED ASPARAGUS WITH PARMESAN

SERVES 4

Store fresh asparagus in the refrigerator or it will lose half its vitamin C and much of its flavour in just two or three days.

1 pound	asparagus, trimmed and bottom half of stalks thinly peeled	500 g
	1 medium red pepper, seeded and cut lengthways into thin strips	
1 tbsp	olive oil	15 mL
1 tbsp	balsamic vinegar	15 mL
1 ounce	Parmesan cheese, in one piece	30 g
	Black pepper, to taste	

86 calories per serving

1 Preheat oven to 500°F (240°C). Place asparagus and pepper strips in a large shallow baking dish. Drizzle with the oil and toss to coat.

2 Roast until crisp-tender, or 10 to 12 minutes, turning occasionally. Transfer to a serving dish.

3 Sprinkle with vinegar. Toss to coat. Using a vegetable peeler, shave cheese into thin curls over vegetables. Season with pepper.

PER SERVING: 6 g protein, 7 g total fat, 2 g saturated fat, 7 mg cholesterol, 3 g carbohydrates, 2 g fibre.

SWAP THE GUAC

● ● ● For a twist on classic guacamole, chop cooked asparagus very finely, add just a little avocado, and season as you would a traditional guacomole. Less fat, more fibre!

MAX OUT ON NUTRIENTS

When you trim the tough ends from asparagus stalks, save them and cook them in water until very tender. Use this vitamin B-enriched water to boost the nutrition of an asparagus (or other) soup or pasta sauce.

TOFU & VEGETABLE STIR-FRY

SERVES 4

If your family is not tempted by tofu, win them over with this Chinese-style dish. The tofu is glazed with ginger and soy, and served on a bed of garlicky noodles and crisp vegetables tossed with plum sauce. It's quick, and cleanup is a snap!

370 calories per serving

²/₃ cup	water	160 mL
8 ounces	firm tofu, cut into large cubes	250 g
2 tbsp	salt-reduced soy sauce	30 mL
2 tbsp	tomato paste	30 mL
2 tbsp	canola oil	30 mL
	3 cloves garlic, minced	
2 tsp	grated fresh ginger	10 mL
6 ounces	wok-ready thin Chinese egg noodles	175 g
7 ounces	broccoli florets, cut into small pieces	200 g
7 ounces	carrots, cut into thin matchsticks	200 g
	1 red pepper, halved, seeded, and thinly sliced	
²/₃ cup	salt-reduced vegetable stock	150 mL
¼ cup	plum sauce	60 mL
7 ounces	baby bok choy, thickly sliced	200 g
	4 green onions, cut into thin lengths	
1 tsp	sesame seeds (optional)	5 mL

INGREDIENT INTEL

Canola has a high smoke point, which makes it suitable for stir-frying. Other oils with high smoke points include corn, peanut, soybean, and safflower.

1 Preheat a grill pan or turn on the oven broiler. Line the grill pan with foil. Using a small knife, mark both sides of each tofu cube with a crisscross pattern and place on the foil. Fold up the edges of the foil to capture the cooking juices.

2 In a small bowl, mix together 1 tbsp (15 mL) each of the soy sauce, tomato paste, and canola oil. Add one-third of the garlic and all of the ginger and mix well to combine. Brush the mixture on the top and bottom of the tofu cubes and set aside while preparing the vegetables.

3 Cook the noodles according to the package instructions. Set aside until needed.

4 Heat the remaining canola oil in a wok or large frying pan over high heat. Add the broccoli and stir-fry for 2 minutes. Add the carrots, pepper, and remaining garlic and stir-fry for 2 minutes, then stir in the stock, remaining soy sauce, and tomato paste. Add the plum sauce and continue to stir-fry for 1 minute, or until the vegetables start to soften.

5 Add the noodles and bok choy to the wok, then stir in three-quarters of the green onions and stir-fry for 2 minutes, or until the bok choy has just wilted. Remove the wok from the heat and keep warm.

6 Put the tofu on the grill or under the broiler and cook for 2 minutes. Flip and grill the other side for 1 minute. Sprinkle the sesame seeds over the top and cook for a further 1 minute.

7 Spoon the vegetables and noodles into bowls, place a piece of tofu in the centre of each and garnish with the remaining green onions. Serve immediately.

PER SERVING: 17 g protein, 15 g total fat, 2 g saturated fat, 0 g cholesterol, 42 g carbohydrates, 8 g fibre.

MUSTARD-GLAZED BRUSSELS SPROUTS & NEW POTATOES

SERVES 4

Cancer-fighting phytochemicals are in plentiful supply in this dish.

10 ounces	Brussels sprouts, halved if large	300 g
12 ounces	red or white new potatoes, unpeeled and halved if large	375 g
1 tbsp	olive oil	30 mL
1 tbsp	finely chopped shallots or onion	30 mL
2 ounces	lean ham or prosciutto, trimmed and chopped	60 g
2 tsp	Dijon mustard	10 mL
¼ tsp	salt	1 ml
	Pinch of black pepper	

133 calories per serving

1 Steam Brussels sprouts and new potatoes until tender, 8 to 10 minutes. Drain.

2 Heat oil in large non-stick frying pan over medium-high heat. Add shallots. Sauté until softened, or 2 to 3 minutes. Stir in ham and mustard. Add Brussels sprouts, potatoes, salt and pepper and continue cooking until everything is hot, about 2 minutes. Serve at once.

PER SERVING: 7 g protein, 6 g total fat, 1 g saturated fat, 8 mg cholesterol, 13 g carbohydrates, 4 g fibre.

ROASTED TOMATOES WITH GARLIC & HERBS

SERVES 4

Slow-roasting fresh tomatoes in olive oil concentrates nutrients and makes them readily available to the body.

3 pounds Italian (plum) tomatoes, halved lengthwise		1.5 kg
2 tbsp	olive oil	30 mL
5 cloves garlic, finely chopped		
½ cup	finely chopped basil	60 mL
2 tbsp	finely chopped rosemary	30 mL
1 tsp	sugar	5 mL
Salt, to taste		

148 calories per serving

1 Preheat oven to 250°F (120°C). Line a jelly roll pan with foil.

2 Toss tomato halves with oil, garlic, basil, rosemary, sugar, and salt in a large bowl. Place, cut side up, in prepared pan. Bake for about 3 hours, or until they have collapsed and their skins have wrinkled. Serve at room temperature or refrigerate and serve chilled.

PER SERVING: 4 g protein, 8 g total fat, 1 g saturated fat, 0 mg cholesterol, 19 g carbohydrates, 5.5 g fiber.

1 MORE IDEA

● ● ● Combine tomato juice and carrot juice and chill. Serve as a refreshing summer soup garnished with chopped tomatoes and a dollop of yogurt.

CUCUMBER, RADISH & SNOW PEA SALAD

SERVES 8

Snow peas and radishes are great sources of folate and vitamin C, nutrients that work together to protect the health of your heart.

6 ounces	snow peas, trimmed	175 g
1 tbsp	rice vinegar	15 mL
2 tsp	sugar	10 mL
2 tsp	soy sauce	10 mL
1 tsp	dark sesame oil	5 mL
	Pinch of salt	
	2 cucumbers, scored and thinly sliced	
	2 bunches radishes, thinly sliced	
	GARNISH	
1 tbsp	sesame seeds, toasted	15 mL

64 calories per serving

1 Cook snow peas in a saucepan of lightly salted boiling water until crisp-tender, or 2 to 3 minutes. Drain. Rinse under cold running water.

2 For the vinaigrette, whisk the vinegar, sugar, soy sauce, sesame oil and salt in a bowl until sugar and salt are dissolved.

3 Combine the snow peas, cucumber, and radish in a large bowl. Add vinaigrette and toss to combine. Sprinkle with sesame seeds, if using.

PER SERVING: 3 g protein, 2 g total fat, 0 g saturated fat, 0 mg cholesterol, 10 g carbohydrates, 3 g fibre.

1 MORE IDEA

● ● ● Here's a refreshing summer treat when your cucumber plants are in peak form: slice thinly and marinate them an hour or two, or overnight, in a 50:50 mixture of water and vinegar (cider or white), adding a hint of sugar to mellow the mix.

WHOLE FOOD
As most gardeners know, you can eat the entire pod of any pea if it's young and tender enough. So if you grow your own, you don't have to wait two months before enjoying their sweet snap.

GRILLED VEGETABLES WITH BALSAMIC GLAZE SERVES 4

Boost your supply of vitamin C and B with this colourful Mediterranean-style combination of vegetables.

101 calories per serving

1 large red pepper, seeded and cut in 1-inch (2.5-cm)-wide strips		
1 medium zucchini, thinly sliced		
1 medium red onion, thinly sliced		
2 medium portobello mushrooms, stems removed and caps cut into 1-inch (2.5-cm)-wide strips		
2 tbsp	extra virgin olive oil	30 mL
1 tsp	dried oregano, crumbled	5 mL
1 tbsp	balsamic vinegar	15 mL
¼ tsp	salt	1 mL
¼ tsp	black pepper	1 mL

INGREDIENT INTEL
Peppers have a naturally waxy skin, which helps to protect them against oxidation and stops vitamin C from being lost during storage, so their vitamin C remains high even several weeks after harvesting.

1 Turn on oven broiler or preheat barbecue. Lightly coat a grill rack with non-stick cooking spray.

2 Combine pepper, zucchini, onion, and mushroom in a large bowl. Sprinkle with oil and oregano. Toss to coat. Place vegetables on the rack in a single layer.

3 Broil or barbecue about 2 inches (5 cm) from heat until vegetables are just crisp-tender and lightly flecked with brown, or 6 to 8 minutes. Turn over; cook until done, about 5 minutes.

4 Arrange vegetables on a platter. Mix the balsamic vinegar, salt, and pepper in a small bowl. Brush over vegetables. Serve warm or at room temperature.

PER SERVING: 2 g protein, 7 g total fat, 1 g saturated fat, 0 mg cholesterol, 8 g carbohydrates, 3 g fibre.

TOMATO SCONES

MAKES 12 SCONES

Bits of fresh tomato add antioxidant power while yogurt adds calcium to every bite.

	1 medium tomato, seeded and finely chopped	
2 cups	all-purpose flour	500 mL
1 tbsp	baking powder	15 mL
½ tsp	salt	2 mL
1 cup	low-fat plain yogurt	250 mL
⅓ cup	olive oil	80 mL
2 tbsp	finely chopped green onion	30 mL
1 tbsp	finely chopped sun-dried tomato	15 mL

145 calories per scone

1 Preheat oven to 425°F (220°C). Lightly coat a baking tray with non-stick cooking spray. Drain the chopped fresh tomato on paper towels.

2 Combine flour, baking powder, and salt in a medium bowl. Combine yogurt and oil in a small bowl; stir into flour mixture just until evenly moistened.

3 Stir fresh tomato, green onion, and sun-dried tomato into flour mixture. Drop dough, ¼ cup (60 mL) at a time, onto the prepared baking tray, making 12 scones.

4 Bake until the tops are golden brown, about 12 minutes. Serve warm or at room temperature.

PER SERVING: 3 g protein, 7 g total fat, 1 g saturated fat, 1 mg cholesterol, 18 g carbohydrates, 1 g fibre.

Good habits are contagious

▶ **A study in the *Journal of American Dietetics Association* showed that women with the highest milk consumption and the lowest intake of sugary beverages took in significantly more of the key nutrients provided by milk. These same women, it turns out, also made healthier choices when it came to other foods. Could one good habit lead to another?**

FOCACCIA WITH TOMATOES & PARSLEY

Focaccia is a flat bread similar to a pizza, but softer and thicker.

2 tsp	sugar	10 mL
2 cups	lukewarm water	500 mL
	1 envelope active dry yeast	
⅓ cup	chopped parsley	75 mL
3 ½ tbsp	olive oil	52 mL
1 ½ tsp	salt	7 mL
½ tsp	dried sage	2 mL
5 cups	all-purpose flour	1.25 L
	2 cloves garlic, crushed	
	3 medium tomatoes, thinly sliced	
	1 large yellow pepper, seeded and cut in thin strips	
2 tbsp	grated Parmesan cheese	30 mL

395 calories per serving

INGREDIENT INTEL
Parsley's high chlorophyll content may explain its use as a breath freshener.

1 Stir sugar into lukewarm water in a large bowl. Sprinkle yeast over the top. Leave until foamy, or about 5 minutes. Stir to dissolve yeast.

2 Reserve 2 tbsp (30 mL) parsley for top of bread. Stir the remaining parsley, 3 tbsp (45 mL) oil, salt and sage into yeast mixture. Add 2 cups flour; mix vigorously. Stir in 3 cups flour to make a stiff dough.

3 Lightly flour a work surface. Knead dough until smooth and elastic (about 10 minutes). Place dough in a lightly oiled bowl; turn to coat then cover loosely. Let rise in a warm place until doubled in volume (about 1 hour, 15 minutes).

4 Lightly oil a jelly roll pan or cookie sheet. Punch dough down, knead briefly, then pat into a rectangle and place in pan. Cover dough loosely with plastic wrap. Let rise in a warm place until doubled in volume (about 40 minutes).

5 Preheat oven to 400°F (200°C). Place oven rack in lowest position. Make dimples in dough with fingertips, brush with remaining oil, then sprinkle with garlic and arrange tomato slices on top. Season with pepper and Parmesan. Bake until edges are browned (35 to 40 minutes). Transfer to a wire rack, sprinkle with reserved parsley, then let cool for at least 20 minutes.

PER SERVING: 11 g protein, 7 g total fat, 1 g saturated fat, 1 mg cholesterol, 71 g carbohydrates, 3 g fibre.

GREEN CORIANDER RICE

Toasting the rice, then cooking with a herb and vegetable paste before adding stock and simmering, develops and enriches the flavour of this dish. The rice makes a great accompaniment to grilled or roast chicken.

165
calories per serving

Basic basmati rice

1 cup (250 mL) brown basmati rice, well rinsed

2 ½ cups (625 mL) water

1 cinnamon stick

8 whole cardamom pods, cracked

Juice of 1 lemon

Boil the water then add rice, cinnamon stick, and cardamom pods. Return to a boil, then cover tightly and cook until the rice is tender, about 10 minutes. Remove the cinnamon stick and drain off excess water. Stir in lemon juice and cover.

1 large green pepper, quartered and seeded		
1 onion, quartered		
1 garlic clove, crushed		
⅓ cup	fresh coriander	75 mL
⅓ cup	flat-leaf parsley	75 mL
2 tsp	reduced-salt margarine	10 mL
2 tsp	extra virgin olive oil	10 mL
1 cup	long-grain white rice	250 mL
2 ⅓ cups	reduced-salt chicken stock, brought to a boil	580 mL
Pepper to taste		
Sprigs fresh cilantro, to garnish		

1 Place the pepper, onion, garlic, cilantro, and parsley in a food processor and blend to a very finely chopped paste. Alternatively, very finely chop them all together with a knife.

2 Heat the margarine and olive oil in a saucepan, add the rice and fry gently for 2 to 3 minutes until the grains are translucent.

3 Remove from the heat and stir in the herb paste. Return to the heat and cook for 2 minutes, stirring constantly. Pour in the stock, and season with pepper. Bring to a boil, then reduce the heat, cover and cook gently for 10 to 15 minutes or until the rice is tender and the stock is absorbed.

4 Remove from the heat and leave to stand, with the pan still covered, for 3 to 4 minutes. Then fork through to separate the grains. Serve hot, garnished with the cilantro sprigs.

PER SERVING: 2 g protein, 1 g total fat, 0 g saturated fat, 0 mg cholesterol, 12 g carbohydrates, 1 g fibre.

MORE GREEN
Green rice can also get its colour from spinach; just stir wilted leaves into the rice after it has absorbed water.

SUMMER RATATOUILLE

SERVES 6

You'll be eating as they do along the Mediterranean with this classic French dish.

	1 large eggplant (about 2 pounds/1 kg)	
¼ tsp	salt	1 mL
	1 small fennel bulb	
4 tsp	olive oil	20 mL
	2 medium yellow squash (8 ounces each), chopped	
	1 medium onion, cut into thin wedges	
3 tbsp	reduced-sodium chicken broth	
	3 large garlic cloves, minced	
1 28-ounce can	no-salt-added tomatoes	1 830-mL
2 tbsp	chopped fresh oregano	20 mL
	1 green pepper, seeded and chopped	
1 tsp	chopped fresh rosemary, plus sprigs	5 mL

132 calories per serving

1 Slice eggplant crosswise. Sprinkle both sides with salt. Set on double layer of paper towels. Let stand 15 minutes then rinse, pat dry with paper towels, and cut into cubes.

2 Trim and chop fennel bulb.

3 Heat 2 tsp (10 mL) oil in large non-stick frying pan over medium-high heat. Sauté squash and onion until onion is soft, about 5 minutes. Transfer to large bowl. Add 1 tsp/5 mL oil and broth to frying pan. Stir in eggplant and reduce heat to medium. Cover and cook, stirring occasionally, until eggplant is tender, about 12 minutes. Add to vegetables in bowl.

4 Add remaining oil and garlic to frying pan and cook 30 seconds. Stir in tomatoes, fennel, oregano, and chopped rosemary, breaking up tomatoes with spoon. Cover and simmer 5 minutes. Stir in green pepper, cover, and simmer 7 minutes longer. Return vegetables to skillet. Simmer, uncovered, 3 minutes, stirring occasionally. Serve warm or at room temperature, garnished with sprigs of rosemary.

PER SERVING: 4 g protein, 4 g total fat, 0.5 g saturated fat, 0 mg cholesterol, 24 g carbohydrates, 8 g fibre.

SUMMER SUPPER SOLUTION

Grilled Pasta Sauce

Put slices of eggplant, zucchini, red pepper, and onion on the grill; cook until tender. Chop and combine with hot pasta and fresh basil. Sprinkle with Parmesan cheese, if desired.

SWAP & DROP

BOK CHOY & MUSHROOM STIR-FRY

SERVES 2

15 ounces/425 g extra-firm tofu

3 tbsp/45 mL reduced-sodium soy sauce

4 tsp/20 mL dark brown sugar

1 ½ tsp/7 mL cornstarch

4 tsp/20 mL olive oil

2 tbsp/30 mL minced fresh ginger

4 green onions, thinly sliced

3 cloves garlic, minced

8 ounces/230 g fresh shiitake mushroom caps, quartered

8 ounces/230 g button mushrooms, halved

¼ tsp/1 mL salt

1 large head bok choy, sliced into 1-inch (2.5-cm) strips

1 Cut the tofu into 12 squares or triangles; set aside. In a small bowl, stir together the soy sauce, brown sugar, cornstarch, and ½ cup (125 mL) of water; set aside.

2 In a large non-stick frying pan, heat 2 tsp (10 mL) of oil over medium heat. Add the ginger, green onions, and garlic, and cook for 1 minute, or until tender. Stir in shiitake and button mushrooms. Add ½ cup (125 mL) of water and salt; cover and cook, stirring occasionally for 5 minutes, or until mushrooms are tender. Transfer to a bowl.

3 Add remaining 2 tsp (10 mL) oil and bok choy to the pan; cook, stirring frequently, for 5 minutes, or until bok choy is tender. Return the mushroom-green onion mix to the pan and add the tofu. Stir the soy sauce mixture to recombine, and add it to the pan. Cook for 2 minutes, or until tofu is hot and the veggies are coated with sauce.

PER SERVING: 20 g protein, 11 g total fat, 1 g saturated fat, 20 g carbohydrates, 4 g fibre.

BULGUR WITH SPRING VEGETABLES

SERVES 6

1 ¼ cups/300 mL bulgur

3 ½ cups/800 mL boiling water

2 tbsp/30 mL olive oil

3 tbsp/45 mL   fresh lemon juice

Salt to taste

½ tsp/2 mL pepper

2 leeks, halved lengthwise, cut crosswise into 1-inch pieces, and well washed

2 cloves garlic, minced

12 asparagus spears, cut into 2-inch/5-cm lengths

1 cup/250 mL frozen peas

¼ cup/60 mL chopped fresh mint

1 Combine bulgur and boiling water in large ovenproof bowl. Let stand until bulgur is tender, about 30 minutes; stir after 15 minutes. Drain bulgur in large fine-meshed sieve to get rid of any remaining liquid.

2 Whisk together 1 tbsp (15 mL) of oil, the lemon juice, salt, and pepper in large bowl. Add drained bulgur and fluff with a fork to separate the grains and combine them with the lemon mixture.

3 Heat remaining 1 tbsp (15 mL) oil in medium skillet over low heat. Add leeks and garlic to skillet and cook until leeks are tender, about 5 minutes. Transfer to bowl with bulgur.

4 In steamer set over a pan of boiling water, steam asparagus until tender, about 4 minutes. Add peas during final 30 seconds of steaming. Add vegetables to bowl of bulgur along with mint and toss to combine. Serve at room temperature or chilled.

PER SERVING: 6 g protein, 5 g total fat, 1 g saturated fat, 32 g carbohydrates, 8 g fibre.

SPICY VEGETABLE COCKTAIL

SERVES 8

The cancer-fighting phytochemical lycopene is highly concentrated in commercial tomato products such as tomato juice.

3 cups	tomato juice	750 mL
¼ cup	coarsely chopped, seeded green pepper	60 mL
	1 green onion, trimmed to 4 inches (10 cm), thinly sliced	
1 tbsp	coarsely chopped parsley	15 mL
1 tbsp	horseradish	15 mL
1 tsp	Worcestershire sauce	5 mL
½ tsp	sugar	2 mL
½ tsp	Tabasco, or to taste	2 mL
	GARNISH	
	Celery stalks and lemon slices	

46 calories per serving

In a blender, process the tomato juice, pepper, green onion, parsley, horseradish, Worcestershire sauce, sugar, and Tabasco until smooth, 2 to 3 minutes. Serve over ice. Garnish with celery and lemon, if desired.

PER SERVING: 2 g protein, 0 g total fat, 0 mg cholesterol, 9 g carbohydrates, 1 g fibre.

INGREDIENT INTEL

Celery contains high concentrations of nutrients, such as potassium and vitamin C. Add more to your diet by making a triple-celery soup: cook sliced celery, celery leaves, garlic, broth, a sprinkling of celery seeds, and herbs (such as marjoran or basil) and purée. Add milk for a creamy soup.

NO-MAYONNAISE CREAMY COLESLAW

SERVES 6

Traditional coleslaw is drowned in a fatty, overly sweet dressing. Ours isn't!

⅓ cup	nonfat plain yogurt	80 mL
4 tsp	Dijon mustard	20 mL
4 tsp	apple cider vinegar	20 mL
4 tsp	extra-virgin olive oil	20 mL
1 ½ tsp	sugar	7 mL
½ tsp	caraway seeds or celery seeds	2 mL
	Salt and pepper, to taste	
4 cups	shredded cabbage (½ medium)	1 L
1 cup	grated carrots (2–4 medium)	250 mL

63 calories per serving

Whisk the yogurt, mustard, vinegar, oil, sugar, caraway seeds, salt, and pepper in a small bowl until smooth. Combine the cabbage and carrots in a large bowl. Add dressing and toss to coat well. One serving is ¾ cup. The coleslaw will keep, covered, in the refrigerator for up to 1 day.

PER SERVING: 2 g protein, 4 g total fat, 1 g saturated fat, 0 mg cholesterol, 7 g carbohydrates, 2 g fibre.

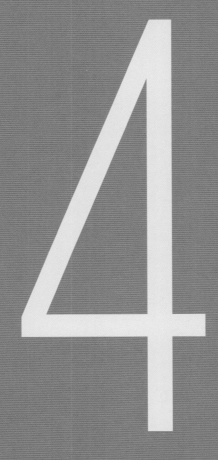

4

SWEETIES

4

Sweeties Let's face it; you don't crave dessert because you're hungry. It's a sheer pleasure

Low-cal desserts don't have to be endless variations of fruit salad. The recipes in this section taste sinfully good. And just about any dessert is within reach of your caloric ideal if you've been treating yourself to our flavourful meals throughout the day.

One word of advice: resist going overboard by enjoying every mouthful. Let each bite linger on your palate.

Take a tip from history. From the time it was first introduced in the 1500s right up to the 1800s, ice cream was enjoyed only by society's elite. It was so outrageously decadent that the rare treat was served in dishes the size of miniature egg cups. A mere spoonful or two—that's all it took to enthrall delighted diners.

These desserts offer a satisfying balance of luxurious tastes and inviting textures coupled with sensible fat and calorie counts.

What better way to sweetly conclude your meal?

Sometimes you just have to eat a little something sweet!

Treat yourself with these better-for-you goodies

Sinfully delicious, mouth-watering treats can stay on the menu when you plan ahead and try these clever swaps that make desserts more nutritious, too.

> "Vegetables are a must on a diet. I suggest carrot cake, zucchini bread, and pumpkin pie. "
>
> —*Jim Davis*

The secret to weight loss isn't restricting specific foods, such as the rich ingredients used to create desserts–it's about planning your menus and controlling portion size. So if you can't live without eating a few sweet treats each week, keep your overall calorie target in mind, and use these great **Swap & Drop** recipes to plan ahead and add an occasional dessert into your weekly menu. And remember, small changes can really add up when baking better-for-you goodies, so here are a few terrific **Swap & Drop** baking hints & tips.

A little swap here... a little swap there

Launch a twin attack against fats. You can try swapping up to one half of fat with applesauce or fruit purée. Or hunt online for recipes that replace oil with mashed banana. If you're trying this in your own recipes, watch your cooking times: when you add fruit your baking times will decrease. You may also want to hold back a bit on the sugar, to compensate for the natural fruit sugars.

Some people just aren't happy with the result and recommend instead simply using less butter, margarine, or oil. Try cutting it by one quarter.

Swap sour cream for yogurt. Mimic even the thickest sour cream by straining low-fat yogurt through cheesecloth.

Reduce the sugar. Start by cutting the sugar by half in both baked goodies and other desserts. If that works well, trim to one quarter to one third. Some find that brown sugar tastes sweeter than white, so less is used. If suitable, you can compensate by boosting the flavour with a little added vanilla, almond extract, orange zest, or cinnamon. (Don't cut sugar when making ice cream, which needs it to achieve the right consistency.)

Swap higher-fat milk for low-fat. Aim to match the consistency of the milk or cream called for, to ensure the best baking result. You can try skim, 1%, evaporated skim, or fat-reduced or fat-free creams.

Swap white flour for whole-wheat, or add a handful of wheat germ or ground flaxseed. Choose to view the more speckled appearance as an added attraction!

Swap sugar with SPLENDA® Sweeteners

What you should know about using SPLENDA® No Calorie Sweetener:

To make your baked goodies brown, lightly spray the batter or dough with cooling spray before baking. (Browning is due to caramelized sugar.)

To make your cakes rise well, use a smaller pan than called for, or add ½ cup non-fat dry milk powder and ½ teaspoon baking soda per cup of SPLENDA® No Calorie Sweetener, Granulated.

Don't worry if you notice your mixture separating when blending eggs, sugar, and fat. It's normal and won't affect your end result.

SPLENDA® No Calorie Sweetener can't activate yeast! Use at least 2 teaspoons of sugar for yeast-rising dough.

Baked goods bake faster, by as much as 5 to 10 minutes.

Or, rethink your sweet fix

Sometimes all you need is a taste. Two squares of a 70 percent dark chocolate bar have 106 calories. A slice of chocolate fudge cake can set you back 490.

VS SALT *Substitutes*

TRADITIONAL BAKING RELIES ON SALT. Most recipes with flour include some salt, often up to a teaspoon or more. You can simply trim the amount to a few grinds of the salt mill (where less seems like more), but if you're tempted by salt substitutes be aware of two things. Firstly, substitutes (not flavour enhancers, which are herbs) are made of various amounts of potassium chloride, which is dangerous for those with heart or kidney problems. Secondly, the more potassium chloride, the more bitter the taste; and the bitter taste worsens when it's heated. So, in baking, salt in moderation may be your best option.

TIME SAVER TIP
You can use bottled cherries instead, thickening them in the same way, using their liquid in place of the water.

CREAMY BAKED CUSTARDS

SERVES 6

These creamy baked custards accompanied by a fresh cherry compote are an easy crowd pleaser. Ideal for dinner parties, they can be prepared ahead of time and refrigerated until serving

2 cups	1% milk	500 mL
1 vanilla bean, split, or 1 tsp (5 mL) vanilla extract		
2 eggs		
2 egg yolks		
3 tbsp	sugar	45 mL
½ tsp	flour	2 mL
COMPOTE		
1 tbsp	sugar	15 mL
1 pound	fresh cherries, pitted	500 g
2 tsp	cornstarch	10 mL
7 tbsp	water	105 mL

165 calories per serving

1 Place milk and vanilla bean in a saucepan and heat until near boiling. Remove from heat, cover, and set aside to infuse for 15 minutes. Remove bean. Alternatively, use extract.

2 Preheat oven to 325°F (160°C). Place the whole eggs, egg yolks, 3 tbsp (45 mL) sugar, and flour in a bowl and lightly whisk together.

3 Bring milk back to near boiling, and slowly pour the hot milk over the egg mixture, whisking constantly. Strain the mixture into a pitcher, then divide among six 4-ounce (125-mL) ramekin dishes coated with cooking spray.

4 Set the ramekins in a shallow roasting pan and pour enough hot water into the pan to come halfway up the sides of the ramekins. Bake until the custards are lightly set, about 30 to 35 minutes. The custards should be slightly wobbly in the centre as they will continue to cook for a few minutes after being removed from the oven. Lift the custards out of the pan of hot water and place on a wire rack to cool. After cooling, refrigerate until ready to serve.

5 For the compote: Place 1 tbsp (15 mL) sugar and 6 tbsp (90 mL) water in a medium saucepan and heat over medium-high heat until the sugar has dissolved. Bring to a boil, then reduce the heat to low and add cherries. Cover the pan and simmer gently, stirring occasionally, until the cherries are tender, 4 to 5 minutes. Use a slotted spoon to remove the cherries and place them in a small serving bowl; set aside.

6 Mix the cornstarch with 1 tbsp (15 mL) cold water and then stir mixture into the cherry juices in the saucepan. Bring the mixture to a boil, then reduce the heat to low and simmer, stirring, until thickened and clear, about 1 minute. Allow to cool for a few minutes, then pour the sauce over the cherries. (The compote can be served warm or at room temperature.) Spoon a little of the cherry compote over the top of each custard, and serve the rest of the compote on the side.

PER SERVING: 7 g protein, 5 total fat, 1 g saturated fat, 145 mg cholesterol, 25 g carbohydrates, 2 g fibre.

SWAP IT OUT!

● ● ● **Chocolate Custard Pots with Poached Pears**

Flavour the milk with a thin strip of pared orange zest instead of the vanilla bean. In Step 2, use light brown sugar, and add 1 tbsp (15 mL) sifted cocoa powder. Continue making the custards as in the main recipe. For the pears, heat 1 cup (250 mL) water with 2 tbsp (30 mL) sugar and a split vanilla bean until the sugar dissolves, then bring to a boil and simmer for 2 to 3 minutes. Add 4 small, firm dessert pears, peeled, cored and thickly sliced. Cover and simmer gently until just tender, about 12 to 15 minutes, turning the pear slices in the syrup occasionally. Lift out the pears with a slotted spoon and transfer to a serving dish. Simmer the syrup for 5 minutes to reduce slightly, then cool for 5 minutes. Remove the vanilla bean and pour over the pears.

FIG BARS

The natural sweetness and full flavour of dried figs need little embellishment other than lemon juice to add a zesty tang.

1 cup	white flour	250 mL
1 cup	whole-wheat flour	250 mL
⅓ cup	light margarine	75 mL
⅓ cup	unsweetened applesauce	75 mL
⅓ cup	light brown sugar	75 mL
1 tsp	vanilla extract	5 mL
	1 egg	
1 8-ounce	package dried figs, finely chopped	250 g
2 tbsp	lemon juice	30 mL

104 calories per bar

1 Sift flours into a mixing bowl. Using two knives or a pastry blender, cut in the margarine until the mixture resembles coarse meal.

2 Add applesauce, sugar, vanilla extract, and egg, and mix to form a firm dough, adding 1 to 2 tsp (5 to 10 mL) water, if necessary, to bind. Wrap dough in plastic; refrigerate for 30 minutes.

3 Place figs in a small saucepan with 6 tbsp (90 mL) water. Bring to a boil, then simmer gently until figs have plumped up slightly and absorbed the water, about 3 to 5 minutes. Transfer to a bowl and mash lightly with a fork to break up the pieces. Add the lemon juice and stir; let cool.

4 Preheat the oven to 375°F (190°C). Roll out the dough on a lightly floured surface to a 20 x 6-inch (50 x 15-cm) rectangle. Cut the dough rectangle in half lengthwise to make 2 strips.

5 Spoon half the fig purée evenly over half of each strip, along one of the long sides. Bring the opposite long side up and over the filling, to form a log shape, and press the edges of the dough together to seal.

6 Flatten each of the logs slightly. Using a sharp knife, cut each log across into 10 bars and transfer to a baking sheet coated with cooking spray. Prick each bar with a fork or score with a sharp knife. Bake until slightly darkened in colour, about 12 to 15 minutes. Transfer the bars to a wire rack to cool. Keep in an airtight container.

PER SERVING: 2 g protein, 2 g total fat, 0.5 g saturated fat, 11 mg cholesterol, 21 g carbohydrates, 2 g fibre.

SWAP
Flavours

TO MAKE CHERRY AND APPLE ROLLS, simmer ½ cup (125 mL) dried cherries in a saucepan with ⅓ cup (75 mL) water and 1 cored and finely chopped apple until the water is absorbed. Use instead of the fig filling.

SWAP & DROP

GOOD

LIGHTENED-UP CHOCOLATE MOUSSE

SERVES 6

1 cup/250 mL dark chocolate chips

1 package soft tofu

⅓ cup/75 mL sugar

¼ cup/60 mL 1% milk

1 tsp/5 mL vanilla extract

½ tsp/2 mL cinnamon

¼ tsp/1 mL cayenne

3 sheets phyllo pastry

¼ cup/60 mL vegetable oil

½ cup/125 mL raspberries

1 Melt chocolate chips in a microwave or on the stovetop over very low heat, stirring constantly until smooth. Put melted chocolate, tofu, sugar, milk, vanilla, cinnamon, and cayenne into a blender and mix until very smooth. Transfer to a bowl and refrigerate until set, an hour or more.

2 When mousse is set, preheat oven to 375°F/190°C. Place one sheet of thawed phyllo pastry on a work surface; keep remaining sheets covered with a damp kitchen towel to keep them moist. Brush a little oil over the surface of the sheet and cover with another sheet of phyllo. Repeat so you have three layers.

3 With a sharp knife, cut layered sheet into quarters, then slice each quarter in half, for 8 pieces in all. Tuck each into a medium-sized muffin cup lightly coated with cooking spray.

4 Bake phyllo until crisp and golden, about 10 minutes. Let cool, then spoon mousse into cups and top with raspberries.

PER SERVING: 2 g protein, 18 g total fat, 7 g saturated fat, 0 mg cholesterol, 33 g carbohydrates, 1 g fibre.

BETTER

CITRUS MOUSSE PARFAIT

SERVES 6

1 tsp/5 mL unflavoured gelatin

2 tbsp/30 mL lemon juice

2 eggs, separated

⅔ cup/150 mL SPLENDA® No Calorie Sweetener, Granulated

½ cup/125 mL orange juice

2 tsp/ 10 mL grated lemon rind

½ cup/125 mL light sour cream

2 cups/500 mL blueberries, raspberries, or sliced strawberries

1 Sprinkle gelatin over lemon juice in small bowl; set aside. In small heavy saucepan, whisk together egg yolks, SPLENDA® No Calorie Sweetener and orange juice. Cook and stir over medium heat until thickened. Remove from heat, stir in softened gelatin until dissolved. Stir in lemon rind.

2 Pour into bowl and place in a pan of ice water to cool and thicken slightly, 5 to 10 minutes. Stir in sour cream.

3 Beat egg whites until stiff peaks form; fold in citrus mixture. In parfait glasses or dessert dishes, layer fruit and mousse mixture. Refrigerate at least 2 hours.

PER SERVING: 4 g protein, 3 g total fat, 2 g saturated fat, 68 mg cholesterol, 10 g carbohydrates, 4 g fibre.

DOUBLE BERRY SAUCE

SERVES 4

For a more complex flavour to top the panna cotta (p. 237), try this compote, which is also delicious served over frozen yogurt, angel food cake, and meringues.

2 tsp	cornstarch	10 mL
1/4 cup	SPLENDA® No Calorie Sweetener, Granulated	60 mL
1/3 cup	water	75mL
1 cup	fresh or frozen blueberries	250 mL
2 cups	sliced strawberries	500 mL
2 tbsp	amaretto or orange-flavoured liqueur	30 mL

51 calories per serving

1 In small heavy saucepan, combine cornstarch, SPLENDA® No Calorie Sweetener, and water. Stir in blueberries. Cook and stir over medium heat until mixture comes to a boil. Simmer until thickened and clear, about 3 minutes.

2 Remove from heat, stir in strawberries and liqueur. Cover and chill.

PER SERVING: 0 g protein, 0 g total fat, 6 g carbohydrates, 1.7 g fibre.

:) BEAUTY ON ICE

Chill drinks with style by placing a few blueberries in each section of an ice cube tray, fill with lemonade and freeze. Drop some cubes in a glass and fill with lemonade or water.

CARAMEL & NUT POPCORN

MAKES 9 CUPS/2 1/4 L

Sample a handful of this sticky treat while cosily seated by the fire.

1/2 cup	SPLENDA® Brown Sugar Blend	125 mL
1/4 tsp	salt	1 mL
1/4 cup	unsalted butter	60 mL
1/4 cup	pineapple juice	60 mL
8 cups	popcorn	2 L
1/4 cup	chopped nuts, such as pecans, peanuts	60 mL

86 calories per serving

1 Mix SPLENDA® Brown Sugar Blend, salt, butter, and juice in a saucepan. Bring to a boil for 8 to 9 minutes without stirring.

2 Remove from the stove, add nuts. Place the popcorn on parchment paper and carefully spread the mixture on the popcorn with a spoon. Set aside to air cool for 10 minutes or until the caramel has hardened.

3 Shape into little balls if desired. Stores well in airtight containers.

PER SERVING (1/4 CUP/60 ML): 0.1 g protein, 4.6 g total fat, 2 g saturated fat, 7 mg cholesterol, 9 g carbohydrates, 0.6 g fibre.

GINGER PANCAKE WITH BANANA TOPPING

SERVES 6

Serve this oversized pancake for dessert for six people.

267
calories per serving

⅓ cup	walnuts	75 mL
½ cup	flour	125 mL
½ cup	1% milk	125 mL
	1 large egg	
	1 large egg white	
1 tbsp	light olive oil	15 mL
1 tbsp	butter, melted	15 mL
2 tsp	sugar	20 mL
1 tsp	vanilla extract	5 mL
¼ tsp	salt	1 mL
⅓ cup	crystallized ginger, finely chopped	75 mL
¼ cup	lime juice, fresh squeezed	60 mL
2 tbsp	packed light brown sugar	30 mL
	3 bananas, thinly sliced	

1 Preheat the oven to 350°F (180°C). Toast walnuts for 5 minutes, or until crisp and fragrant. When cool enough to handle, chop coarsely. Increase the oven temperature to 425°F (220°C). Lightly oil a 10-inch (25-cm) non-stick skillet and place it in the oven.

2 In a large bowl, stir together flour, milk, egg, egg white, oil, butter, sugar, vanilla, and salt until well combined. Stir in the ginger.

3 Pour the batter into the hot pan, return the pan to the oven, and bake for 12 to 15 minutes, or until the pancake has puffed and is golden brown.

4 Meanwhile, in a large skillet, combine the lime juice and brown sugar, and cook over medium heat until the sugar has melted. Add the sliced bananas and cook for 3 minutes, or until the bananas have softened. Stir in the walnuts. To serve, cut the pancake into wedges and top with the banana-walnut mixture.

PER SERVING: 3 g protein, 10 g total fat, 2.4 g saturated fat, 42 mg cholesterol, 42 g carbohydrates, 2 g fibre.

1 MORE IDEA

● ● ● **Hot banana sundae**
Spit an unpeeled banana length-wise and insert a few pieces of dark chocolate. Wrap tightly in foil and bake at 300°F (150°C) for 20 minutes. Scoop hot banana and melted chocolate onto low-fat vanilla frozen yogurt.

Butterscotch ripple ice cream
195 calories
7.5 g fat
4.5 g saturated fat

FLAVOUR CHECKER

COOLING SCOOPS

You've gotta love a frozen treat in summer, preferably often.
But do you know what you're getting yourself into with the various types available? We compared a few in measures of ¾ cup (175 mL) each.

Using tiny spoons like these can help you slow down and savour each bite.

Orange sorbet
135 calories
0 g total fat

Chocolate-chocolate chunk extra-rich ice cream
450 calories
30 g fat
15 g saturated fat

Lemon gelato
90 calories
0 g total fat

With gelato, generally only the fruit-flavoured ones like this are 0 fat; other varieties have 4 or 5 g of fat.

Black cherry frozen yogurt
150 calories
1.5 g fat
1 g saturated fat

Maple frozen soy dessert
195 calories
7.5 g fat
6 g saturated fat

BLUEBERRY BAVARIAN

Spoon up a tangy-sweet mouthful of our custardy berry blend and discover how sublime a heart-friendly dessert can be. Instead of heavy cream and whole eggs, we use low-fat milk, dry milk, sour cream, and gelatin.

1 cup	1% milk	250 mL
¼ cup	fat-free dry milk	60 mL
2 12-ounce	packages frozen blueberries, thawed	2 340-g
½ cup plus 1 tbsp	sugar	125 mL plus 15 mL
	Salt, to taste	
1 cup	fat-free sour cream	250 mL
	1 package unflavoured gelatin	
¼ cup	cold water	60 mL
½ cup	fresh blueberries	125 mL

270 calories per ramekin

1 Combine milk and dry milk in small bowl and whisk until well blended. Place in freezer for up to 30 minutes.

2 Combine frozen blueberries, ½ cup (125 mL) sugar, and salt in medium saucepan over low heat. Bring to a simmer and cook until sugar has dissolved, berries have broken up, and mixture has reduced to 2 ¼ cups (560 mL), about 10 minutes. Let cool to room temperature. Stir in ⅔ cup (160 mL) sour cream.

3 Sprinkle gelatin over ¼ cup (60 mL) cold water in heatproof measuring cup. Let stand 5 minutes to soften. Set measuring cup in small saucepan of simmering water and heat until gelatin has melted, about 2 minutes. Let cool to room temperature.

4 With a hand mixer, beat chilled milk until thick, soft peaks form. Beat in remaining 1 tbsp (15 mL) sugar until stiff peaks form. Beat in gelatin mixture. Fold milk mixture into blueberry mixture.

5 Spoon into 6 dessert ramekins or glasses. Chill until set, about 2 hours. At serving time, top each with a dollop of remaining sour cream and fresh blueberries.

EACH SERVING: 4 g protein, 6 g total fat, 4g saturated fat, 6 mg cholesterol, 38 g carbohydrates, 3 g fibre.

HOW TO MIMIC HEAVY CREAM

By adding dry milk to low-fat milk, you get a thick milk when chilled that can be whipped and used like heavy cream. The mixture is stabilized with gelatin to keep it firm.

SWAP IT OUT!

● ● ● **Strawberry/Peach Bavarian**

Use 2 packages of either frozen strawberries or peaches for the filling and top with fresh blueberries and diced fresh peaches.

PEACH & RICOTTA CRÊPES

This crêpe recipe is very easy to make and the batter will keep in the fridge overnight. You can freeze any extras for future use.

230 calories per crêpe

	CRÊPES	
½ cup	whole-wheat flour	125 mL
	1 egg	
½ cup	milk	125 mL
¼ cup	water	60 mL
2 tsp	butter, divided	10 mL
	FILLING	
	3 peaches, peeled, pitted and thinly sliced	
1 tsp	vanilla extract	5 mL
½ cup	low-fat ricotta	125 mL
1 tsp	lemon zest	5 mL
¼ cup	maple syrup	60 mL

SWAP
up Flavours

IF YOU HAVE SOME BRANDY OR GRAND MARNIER, add a splash to the peaches while cooking for an extra kick.

1 In a medium-sized mixing bowl, whisk together flour and egg. Gradually add milk and water, and whisk till smooth. Heat an 8-inch (20-cm) non-stick pan over medium heat. Melt 1 tsp (5 mL) of butter in pan, then absorb butter with a paper towel by lightly patting it on the pan. Pour ¼ cup (60 mL) of batter into pan for each crêpe (you should have enough for four). Holding pan by the handle, whirl it in a circular motion so the batter coats the surface of pan evenly. Cook crêpe for about one minute, until the bottom is light brown. Lift with a spatula, flip and cook the other side. Place finished crêpes to the side on a plate.

2 Once all four crêpes are made, melt the remaining 1 tsp (5 mL) of butter in the pan on medium heat and add peach slices. Sauté, turning regularly until soft. Reserve eight slices for garnish, and transfer the rest to a medium bowl.

3 Add vanilla, ricotta and lemon zest, and stir. Place each crêpe on its own plate. Divide peach mixture among the four crêpes. Fold each crêpe, with filling inside, into quarters and place two peach slices on top to garnish. Drizzle with maple syrup to taste.

PER SERVING: 9 g protein, 6 g total fat, 3 g saturated fat, 69 mg cholesterol, 39 g carbohydrates, 4 g fibre.

BLUEBERRY-STRAWBERRY MOUSSE

SERVES 4

This is a pretty dessert that takes just minutes to prepare. You can do it as the table is being cleared if you wash the blueberries and slice the strawberries ahead of time.

1 cup	blueberries	250 mL
1 cup	strawberries, sliced	250 mL
1 cup	light cream (5%)	250 mL
1 tbsp	honey	15 mL
½ tsp	cinnamon	2 mL

168 calories per serving

1 Slice strawberries; put fruit in fridge if you are finishing the dessert later.

2 Add half of the blueberries and strawberries to bottom of four dessert dishes (or wine glasses). Set aside. Using an electric hand-held mixer, whip cream, honey, and cinnamon until stiff peaks form.

3 Fold in remaining blueberries and strawberries. Distribute among dishes and garnish each with a couple of blueberries and strawberry slices. Add a sprig of mint, if desired.

PER SERVING: 2 g protein, 12 g total fat, 7 g saturated fat, 15 g carbohydrates, 40 mg cholesterol, 2 g fibre.

WHIPPING CREAM TIP

When you are whipping lower-fat cream, for best results it needs to be really cold. Try putting it in the freezer for a half hour beforehand (any longer and it will begin to freeze).

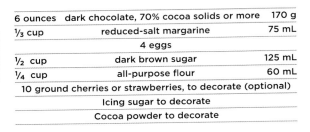

IF YOU'RE MAKING THE TORTE for a special occasion, drizzle 4 tbsp (60 mL) brandy or an orange liqueur such as Cointreau over the top of the cake after baking, then let cool. Or serve it with a **SCOOP OF VANILLA FROZEN YOGURT**, for a dark-versus-light chiaroscuro effect.

SWAP IT OUT!

● ● ● You could use ground almonds instead of flour to vary the flavour, or to accommodate gluten-intolerant eaters.

RICH CHOCOLATE TORTE

SERVES 10

A generous amount of good-quality dark chocolate makes this cake beautifully moist and rich. It's perfect with a cup of coffee, or warm for dessert.

6 ounces	dark chocolate, 70% cocoa solids or more	170 g
⅓ cup	reduced-salt margarine	75 mL
	4 eggs	
½ cup	dark brown sugar	125 mL
¼ cup	all-purpose flour	60 mL
	10 ground cherries or strawberries, to decorate (optional)	
	Icing sugar to decorate	
	Cocoa powder to decorate	

225 calories per slice

1 Preheat the oven to 350°F (180°C). Grease a 10-inch (25-cm) springform cake pan and line it with greased parchment paper.

2 Break up the chocolate and place it in a heatproof bowl with the margarine. Set the bowl over a saucepan of almost boiling water, making sure the water does not touch the base of the bowl. Leave to melt, then remove from the heat and stir the mixture until smooth.

3 Meanwhile, place the eggs and sugar in a large bowl and beat with an electric mixer until the mixture has increased considerably in volume and leaves a trail on the surface when the beaters are lifted out. (If using a whisk or egg beater, set the bowl over a saucepan of almost boiling water, making sure the water is not touching the base of the bowl.)

4 Add the chocolate mixture and fold in with a large metal spoon. Gradually sift the flour over the top of the mixture, folding it in until it is just combined.

5 Turn the mixture into the prepared cake pan, gently spreading it to the edges to level the surface. Bake for 15 to 20 minutes or until the top of the cake feels just firm to the touch. Leave to cool in the pan.

6 Remove the cake from the pan and peel away the parchment paper. Cut into thin wedges for serving, decorating each with a ground cherry or strawberry, if desired. Dust with the sifted icing sugar and cocoa powder. The cake can be kept in the refrigerator for 2 to 3 days.

PER SERVING: 4 g protein, 14 g total fat, 5 g saturated fat, 87 mg cholesterol, 22 g carbohydrates, 0.4 g fibre.

CHERRY CRISP

Sour cherries (pie cherries)—fresh or frozen—can be substituted for the sweet cherries, but increase the granulated sugar in the cherry mixture to $1/3$ or $1/2$ cup, to taste.

257 calories per serving

1/4 cup	granulated sugar	60 mL
2 tbsp	cornstarch	30 mL
1 tsp	cinnamon	5 mL
1/2 tsp	each, pepper and salt	2 mL
1/8 tsp	allspice	0.5 mL
2 tsp	grated lime zest	10 mL
	2 bags (11 ounces/300 g each) **frozen pitted sweet cherries, thawed**	
1 tbsp	fresh lime juice	15 mL
I cup	old-fashioned rolled oats	250 mL
1/3 cup	flour	75 mL
1/3 cup	firmly packed light brown sugar	75 mL
3 tbsp	cold, unsalted butter, cut up	45 mL

1 Preheat the oven to 400°F (200°C). In a large bowl, stir together the granulated sugar, cornstarch, cinnamon, pepper, 1/4 tsp (1 mL) of the salt, the allspice, and lime zest. Add the cherries and lime juice, tossing to coat. Transfer to a 9 x 9-inch (22 x 22-cm) glass baking dish; set aside.

2 In a medium bowl, stir together the remaining 1/4 tsp (1 mL) salt, the oats, flour, and brown sugar. With a pastry blender or two knives, cut in the butter until the mixture resembles coarse crumbs. Sprinkle the mixture over the fruit.

3 Bake for 25 minutes, or until the fruit is bubbly and piping hot and the topping is golden brown and crisp.

PER SERVING: 4 g protein, 7 g total fat, 4 g saturated fat, 16 mg cholesterol, 48 g carbohydrates, 1.4 g fibre.

VARIATION

● ● ● For an even better-tasting crisp, use fresh cherries. To get the amount of pitted cherries you need here, buy 2 pounds (1 kg) of fresh cherries and pit them; this should yield the same quantity as the 22 ounces (600 g) of frozen pitted cherries.

RASPBERRY KEY LIME CRÊPES

SERVES 6

Key lime juice turns cream cheese into the refreshing filling for these berry crêpes. For an added twist, pipe the sweet filling into phyllo-dough cones that I bake separately for a fun snack.

3 tbsp	key lime juice	45 mL
1 package (12.3 ounces/350 g) silken firm tofu, crumbled		
6 ounces	reduced-fat cream cheese, cubed	170 g
2/3 cup	confectioners' sugar, divided	150 mL
2 1/2 tsp	grated lime peel	12 mL
Dash salt		
Dash ground nutmeg		
6 prepared crêpes (9 inches/23 cm) (see recipe p. 228)		
1 1/2 cups	fresh raspberries	375 mL

222
calories per
filled crêpe

(see recipe p. 228)

The key to key limes

▷ Key limes are smaller and more sour than regular limes. If you need to substitute, use a half-and-half mixture of regular limes and lemons.

1 In a blender, combine lime juice, tofu, and cream cheese; cover and process until smooth. Set aside 1 tsp (5 mL) confectioners' sugar. Add the lime peel, salt, nutmeg, and remaining confectioners' sugar; cover and process until blended. Cover and refrigerate for at least 1 hour.

2 Spread cream cheese mixture over crêpes. Sprinkle with raspberries; roll up. Dust with reserved confectioners' sugar.

PER SERVING: 8 g protein, 9 g total fat, 5 g saturated fat, 26 mg cholesterol, 28 g carbohydrates, 3 g fibre.

BLUEBERRY-ORANGE TART

SERVES 8

Don't be surprised by the touch of pepper in the filling—it heightens the blueberry flavour nicely.

1 ½ cups	flour	375 mL
⅓ cup	icing sugar	75 mL
2 tsp	grated orange zest	10 mL
½ tsp	baking powder	2 mL
¼ tsp	salt	1 mL
¼ cup plus 3 tbsp	olive oil	105 mL
2 tbsp plus ¼ cup	orange juice	30 mL plus 60 mL
2 11-ounce	bags frozen unsweetened blueberries	600 g
8 tbsp	granulated sugar, divided	125 mL
½ tsp	pepper	2 mL
⅛ tsp	nutmeg	0.5 mL
3 tbsp	cornstarch	45 mL

319 calories per slice

Blueberries for supper

▶ Mix blueberries with finely diced red pepper, jalapeno, sweet onion, chopped cilantro, and a squeeze of lime juice. Use as a topping for grilled salmon, chicken, or tofu.

1 In a large bowl, stir together the flour, icing sugar, orange zest, baking powder, and salt. Add the oil and 2 tbsp (30 mL) of the orange juice, and stir until the mixture comes together. Transfer the dough to a lightly floured work surface and knead 10 times, or until the dough forms a ball. Flatten into a disk, wrap in plastic wrap, and let stand for 30 minutes.

2 Preheat the oven to 350°F (180°C). With your fingertips, gently press the dough onto the bottom and sides of a 9-inch (22-cm) tart pan with a removable bottom. Prick the bottom of the shell with a fork and line the pan with foil. Fill the foil with pie weights or dried beans, and bake the shell for 15 minutes. Remove the foil and weights, and bake the shell for another 10 minutes, or until golden brown. Cool on a wire rack.

3 Meanwhile, in a saucepan, combine the blueberries, the remaining ¼ cup (60 mL) orange juice, 6 tbsp (90 mL) of the granulated sugar, the pepper, and nutmeg; bring to a boil. Reduce to a simmer and cook for 5 minutes.

4 In a small bowl, stir together the remaining 2 tbsp (30 mL) sugar and cornstarch. Stir the cornstarch mixture into the berries, and cook for 2 minutes, or until the berry mixture is thick.

5 Cool the blueberry mixture to room temperature, then spoon into the baked shell. Chill the tart for 1 hour before serving.

PER SERVING: 3 g protein, 13 g total fat, 2 g saturated fat, 0 mg cholesterol, 50 g carbohydrates, 3.4 g fibre.

WATERMELON RASPBERRY POPSICLES

A surprising twist on an old freezer favourite.

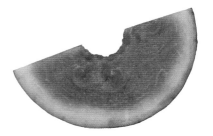

2 cups	watermelon, seeded and diced	500 mL
1 cup	fresh raspberries	250 mL
⅓ cup	SPLENDA® No Calorie Sweetener, Granulated	75 mL
1 tbsp	fresh lemon juice	15 mL
1 tbsp	light corn syrup	15 mL

25 calories per popsicle

1 Place all ingredients in blender or food processor. Blend until smooth. Pour ingredients out of blender. Strain through a sieve into a small bowl, pressing firmly to extract as much of the liquid as possible. Discard pulp.

2 Pour extracted juice into popsicle moulds and freeze at least 6 hours or overnight.

PER SERVING: 0.4 g protein, 0 g total fat, 0 mg cholesterol, 5 g carbohydrates, 1 g fibre.

STRAWBERRY YOGURT PANNA COTTA

When desire for a creamy dessert calls, this could be the answer.

2 cups	sliced fresh or thawed strawberries	500 mL
1/3 cup	SPLENDA® No Calorie Sweetener, Granulated	75 mL
1 cup	Greek-style plain yogurt	250 mL
4 tsp	unflavoured gelatin	20 mL
3/4 cup	5% cream	175 mL
1 tsp	vanilla	5 mL
	BERRY COMPOTE	
1 1/3 cups	sliced fresh or thawed strawberries	330 mL
2 tsp	SPLENDA® No Calorie Sweetener, Granulated	10 mL
1 tbsp	balsamic vinegar	15 mL

111 calories per serving

BERRY NICE BREAKFAST!
Mix maple syrup with Saskatoon berries or blueberries, and add the grated zest of an orange. Microwave until warm. Serve on multi-grain waffles or French toast.

1 In blender, blend strawberries, 1/3 cup (75 mL) SPLENDA® No Calorie Sweetener, and yogurt; strain into bowl; set aside. In small bowl, sprinkle gelatin over 1/4 cup (60 mL) cream; let stand for 5 minutes to soften.

2 In small saucepan, heat remaining cream with vanilla over medium heat until steaming; stir in gelatin mixture until melted. Whisk into strawberry mixture. Pour into six 6-ounce (175-mL) ramekins or moulds. Cover and refrigerate until set, about 4 hours.

3 Make compote: In small bowl, combine strawberries with SPLENDA® No Calorie Sweetener; let stand for 10 minutes. Turn panna cottas out onto dessert plates. Top with berries; sprinkle with vinegar.

PER SERVING: 4 g protein, 4 g total fat, 2 g saturated fat, 17 mg cholesterol, 13 g carbohydrates, 1 g fibre.

PEAR & RED CURRANT PHYLLO LATTICE

SERVES 6

The bright red juice of the currants tints the pears and looks attractive under the pastry lattice. Red currants have a short season, but they freeze well, so put some in the freezer to use later in the year.

170 calories per slice

TART		
	3 sheets phyllo pastry	
	Butter-flavoured cooking spray	
FILLING		
2 tbsp	red-currant jelly (or raspberry jam)	30 mL
1 tsp	lemon juice	5 mL
	3 medium ripe, firm pears	
4 ounces	red currants or gooseberries	125 g
½ cup	ground almonds	125 mL

1 Preheat the oven to 400°F (200°C) and put a baking sheet in to heat. For the filling, place the red-currant jelly and lemon juice in a small saucepan and heat gently over medium heat until melted. Remove from the heat.

2 Peel the pears and slice thinly. Add to the jelly glaze and toss gently to coat. Stir in the red currants.

3 Lay out 2 sheets of phyllo on top of each other. (Keep the third sheet covered to prevent it from drying out.) Cut into quarters. Separate the 8 pieces and coat with cooking spray. Use them to line a 9-inch (23-cm) loose-bottomed tart pan, overlapping them slightly, scrunching and tucking in the edges.

4 Sprinkle the ground almonds over the bottom of the lined tart pan. Top with the pear and red-currant mixture, spreading the fruit out evenly.

5 Cut the remaining sheet of phyllo crosswise in half and spray with cooking spray. Place one half on top of the other, then cut into 10 strips about ³/₄ inch (2 cm) wide, trimming off excess pastry. Twist the doubled strips gently and arrange them in a lattice pattern over the filling, tucking in the ends neatly.

6 Place the pan on the hot baking sheet and bake until the pastry is crisp and golden brown, about 15 to 20 minutes. Serve warm.

PER SERVING: 3 g protein, 6 g total fat, 0 g saturated fat, 0 mg cholesterol, 28 g carbohydrates, 4 g fibre.

SWAP IT OUT!

● ● ● **Mango & Gooseberry Phyllo Tart**

Sprinkle the bottom of the lined tart pan with 3 tbsp (45 mL) shredded coconut. Peel and dice 2 ripe mangoes and mix with 4 ounces (125 g) halved gooseberries. Toss the fruit gently with 2 tbsp (30 mL) each of lime juice and light brown sugar, then spoon into the pastry and spread out evenly. Top with the pastry lattice and bake as in the main recipe.

FRUIT SWAP
Make a pear and raspberry phyllo lattice by using raspberries instead of red currants, and seedless raspberry jam for the glaze rather than redcurrant jelly.

CHOCOLATE TRUFFLES

This mixture also makes a great chocolate spread for kids' treats.

PEARS & CHOCOLATE: A CLASSIC
For a warm dessert on a cold night, halve pears, remove core, and place cut sides down in a baking dish. Bake until slightly soft, about 15 minutes. Flip the fruit over, drizzle with chocolate sauce, and bake 5 minutes more. Sprinkle with chopped pecans.

1 ¼ cups	unsweetened chocolate chips	300 mL
⅔ cup	15% cream	150 mL
1 tbsp	SPLENDA® No Calorie Sweetener, Granulated	15 mL
¼ cup	butter	60 mL
¼ cup	raisins	60 mL
1 tbsp	orange zest	15 mL
	Cocoa for dredging	

150 calories per trio

1 Place chocolate in large bowl. In a small saucepan, bring cream, SPLENDA® No Calorie Sweetener, butter, raisins, and orange zest to a boil.

2 Slowly pour hot cream mixture over chocolate and stir until smooth. Let cool in refrigerator for 2 to 3 hours.

3 Shape mixture into small balls by rolling it, squeezing slightly, between your palms.

4 Dredge in cocoa or, if you're giving truffles as presents, consider rolling some of the truffles in a variety of edibles. Try chopped nuts, such as walnuts and pecans, but be sure to toast them lightly first to draw out their flavour. You can roll them in confectioners' sugar, sprinkles, or candied orange or lemon zest. You can dip them in white chocolate; try to make it as thin a coating as possible.

PER SERVING: 3 g protein, 12 g total fat, 8 g saturated fat, 10 mg cholesterol, 8 g carbohydrates, 3 g fibre.

NUTTY DARK CHOCOLATE COOKIE DELIGHT MAKES 20 SQUARES

A little goes a long way with this crunchy, sweet bar.

COOKIE		
1 ¼ cups	all-purpose flour	300 mL
½ cup	unsalted butter, room temperature	125 mL
½ cup	SPLENDA® Brown Sugar Blend	125 mL

TOPPING		
2 squares unsweetened dark chocolate		
¼ cup	SPLENDA® No Calorie Sweetener, Granulated	60 mL
¼ cup	unsweetened coconut	60 mL
1 ½ cups	ground unsalted nuts (pecans, walnuts, almonds, peanuts)	375 mL
¼ cup	melted butter	60 mL
2 tbsp	35% cream	30 mL

175 calories per square

1 Preheat oven to 350°F (180°C). Mix flour with SPLENDA® Brown Sugar Blend in an 8- or 9-inch (20- or 23-cm) square pan. Add the butter in pieces. Mix with a fork until grainy.

2 Spread evenly in the pan and press down lightly. Bake for 15 minutes or until edges are golden. Let cool.

3 To make topping: Melt chocolate in microwave on a very low setting. Add 2 tbsp (30 mL) SPLENDA® No Calorie Sweetener, Granulated and mix well. Pour melted chocolate on cookie, sprinkle coconut, and top with nuts.

4 In a small bowl, thoroughly mix cream and remaining 2 tbsp (30 mL) SPLENDA® No Calorie Sweetener into melted butter. Spread over nut mixture with a spoon. Bake for 15 to 20 minutes, or until nut mixture is golden brown. Let cool and cut in squares. Store in airtight container.

PER SERVING : 1 g protein, 14 g total fat, 7 g saturated fat, 21 mg cholesterol, 10 g carbohydrates, 2 g fibre.

Nuts to the rescue!

◗ **Need a quick, special dinner? Mix finely chopped pecans with an equal amount of bread crumbs. Roll pieces of fish fillet or boneless chicken breast in lightly beaten egg white, then in nut mixture. Bake at 375°F (190°C) until nicely browned and cooked through.**

CREAM CHEESE RASPBERRY BROWNIES

Sometimes a brownie just calls out for a little special treatment.

5 ounces	semisweet chocolate, chopped	150 g
9 ounces	light cream cheese, softened	250 g
½ cup	SPLENDA® No Calorie Sweetener, Granulated	125 mL
	2 eggs	
1 tsp	vanilla	5 mL
½ cup	butter, softened	125 mL
⅓ cup	seedless raspberry jam	75 mL
⅔ cup	all-purpose flour	160 mL
¼ tsp	baking soda and salt	1 mL
¼ tsp	salt	1 mL

117 calories per square

1 Line 8-inch (20-cm) square cake pan with foil, leaving overhang for handles. Set aside.

2 In heatproof bowl over saucepan of hot (not boiling) water, melt chocolate; let cool slightly. Meanwhile, in separate bowl, beat cream cheese with half of the SPLENDA® No Calorie Sweetener until smooth. Beat in 1 of the eggs and half of the vanilla; set aside.

3 In separate bowl, beat butter with remaining SPLENDA® No Calorie Sweetener until fluffy. Beat in remaining egg. Beat in all but 2 tbsp (30 mL) of the jam and the remaining vanilla, then add the chocolate, mixing well. In small bowl, whisk together flour, baking soda, and salt; mix into chocolate batter just until combined.

4 Spread chocolate batter in prepared pan. Layer with cream cheese mixture. Spoon remaining jam, in small dollops, over top. With a knife, zigzag through cheese and jam layers for marbled effect.

5 Bake in 350°F (180°C) oven until tester inserted in centre has only a few crumbs clinging, about 40 minutes. Let cool in pan on rack. Cover and refrigerate until chilled, about 2 hours. Remove from pan. Cut into squares, wiping knife between slices.

PER SERVING: 2 g protein, 7 g total fat, 5 g saturated fat, 30 mg cholesterol, 10 g carbohydrates, 1 g fibre.

SWAP IT OUT!

● ● ● Drizzle a bowl of raspberries with 1 ounce (30 g) of dark chocolate sauce—a doubly healthy treat.

SPICY FENNEL NUTS

MAKES 3 CUPS

Perfect to titillate your tastebuds before supper, or as an after-dinner perk.

4 tsp	fennel seeds	20 mL
6 tbsp	SPLENDA® No Calorie Sweetener, Granulated	90 mL
¼ tsp	salt	1 mL
1 tsp	ground cinnamon	5 mL
1 tsp	ground cayenne pepper	5 mL
	1 egg white	
2 cups	pecan halves	500 mL
1 cup	whole almonds	250 mL

210 calories per serving

1 Preheat oven to 300°F (150°C).

2 Grind fennel seeds using a mortar & pestle or food processor until mostly ground; they do not need to be a fine powder.

3 Combine the ground fennel seeds with SPLENDA® No Calorie Sweetener, salt, cinnamon and cayenne pepper in a small bowl and set aside.

4 Whip the egg white to moist peaks in a large bowl.

5 Fold the spice mixture into the whipped egg white until thoroughly combined.

6 Add the pecans and almonds and gently mix together until the nuts are thoroughly coated, and then spread evenly over a large baking sheet.

7 Bake for 25 minutes. Halfway through the baking time, use a metal flipper to separate the nuts from the pan and flip.

8 Cool the cooked nut mixture on the pan until they are room temperature. The nuts will become crisp as they cool on the pan. Serve immediately or store in an air-tight container.

PER SERVING (¼ CUP/60 ML): 4.5 g protein, 20 g total fat, 1.5 g saturated fat, 0 mg cholesterol, 7.5 g carbohydrates, 4 g fibre.

SNACK WITH A KICK
Toss a large handful of whole cashews, almonds, or walnuts with 1 tsp (5 mL) each of olive oil and ground cumin, a pinch of salt, and some cayenne pepper. Place in a shallow pan and bake at 350°F (180°C) for 25 to 30 minutes, stirring occasionally.

BLACK CURRANT-MANGO ICED TEA

SERVES 6

Iced tea is always fat-free, but this version stirs it up in the flavour department.

	6 black currant tea bags	
¼ cup	packed fresh mint leaves	60 mL
	4 thin slices of lime	
4 ¾ cups	boiling water	1.175 L
¼ cup	SPLENDA® No Calorie Sweetener, Granulated	60 mL
1 ¼ cups	100% mango juice	300 mL
	Ice cubes	

38 calories per cup/250 mL

1 Place tea bags, mint and lime in large measuring cup or teapot; cover with boiling water and steep for 10 minutes.

2 Strain into large pitcher. Stir in SPLENDA® No Calorie Sweetener until dissolved. Stir in mango juice; serve over ice.

PER SERVING: 0 g protein, 0 total fat, 0 g cholesterol, 10 g carbohydrates, 1 g fibre.

Mango for supper

Balance sweet and spicy by adding chopped mango to your next tofu, chicken, beef, or pork curry made with coconut milk.

◐ ...AND FOR DESSERT

Use an ice cream maker to turn ripe mangoes into a richly flavoured, no-fat sorbet.

CHAMOMILE-POMEGRANATE TEA

SERVES 4

Splendid for summer sipping in the garden.

	4 chamomile tea bags	
3 cups	boiling water	750 mL
1 cup	pomegranate juice	250 mL
⅓ cup	SPLENDA® No Calorie Sweetener, Granulated	75 mL
	Fresh mint sprigs, for garnish	

34 calories per cup/250 mL

1 Place tea bags in a large heatproof measuring cup or pitcher; pour boiling water over tea bags. Steep 1 hour, or until cooled to room temperature. Remove and discard tea bags.

2 Add pomegranate juice, then SPLENDA® No Calorie Sweetener, and stir until it dissolves. Serve over ice; garnish with mint sprigs.

PER SERVING: 0 g protein, 0 g total fat, 0 g cholesterol, 10 g carbohyrates, 0 g fibre.

LIGHT STRAWBERRY JAM

MAKES 6 CUPS/1.5 L

The bright taste of summer, all year long.

4 cups	crushed strawberries	1 L
1 ½ cups	SPLENDA® No Calorie Sweetener, Granulated	375 mL
	1 package freezer jam gelling powder	
1 tsp	grated lemon rind	5 mL

9
calories per tbsp/15 mL

1 Place crushed strawberries in a large bowl. Add grated lemon rind. Stir in SPLENDA® No Calorie Sweetener. Let stand 15 minutes.

2 Slowly sprinkle gelling powder into fruit mixture, while stirring for 3 minutes. Let stand 5 minutes. Stir again for 1 minute.

3 Pour into sterilized jars, leaving ½-inch (1-cm) head space; seal. To sterilize jars, place both lids and jars in boiling water for 15 minutes before filling. Store in freezer for up to 1 year or in the refrigerator for 6 weeks.

PER SERVING: 0 g protein, 0 g total fat, 0 g cholesterol, 2 g carbohydrates, 0.6 g fibre.

NO-COOK LIGHT PEACH JAM

MAKES 4 CUPS/1 L

A great recipe for when you just don't want to heat up the kitchen.

4 cups	ripe peaches	1 L
1 ½ cups	SPLENDA® No Calorie Sweetener, Granulated	375 mL
	1 package jam gelling powder	
¼ cup	almonds, chopped or slivered	60 mL
½ tsp	almond extract	2 mL

12
calories per tbsp/15 mL

1 Peel, pit and finely chop peaches (do not purée). Measure 4 cups (1 L) peaches into large bowl. Stir in SPLENDA® No Calorie Sweetener. Let stand 15 minutes. Slowly sprinkle gelling powder into peaches while stirring for 3 minutes. Stir in almonds and almond extract. Let stand 5 minutes. Stir again for 1 minute.

2 To sterilize jars, place both lids and jars in boiling water for 15 minutes before filling. Pour into sterilized jars, leaving ½ inch (1 cm) headspace; seal. Store in freezer for up to 1 year or in the refrigerator for 6 weeks.

PER SERVING: 0.1 g protein, 0.3 g total fat, 0 g saturated fat, 0 g cholesterol, 2.5 g carbohydrates, 0.7 g fibre.

SWAP IT OUT!

● ● ● **Brandied Peach Jam**

Omit almonds and extract; stir in 1 ½ tbsp (20 mL) brandy.

● ● ● **Ginger Peach Jam**

Omit almonds and extract, if desired; stir in 1 tbsp (15 mL) chopped, candied ginger.

One last Swap!

Vegetables—so good for you, yet usually absent from the sweet foods we crave. Go ahead and add some veggies to these flavourful snacks to achieve surprisingly delectable results.

VELVETY BEET BROWNIES MAKES 16

The chocolate flavour of these moist, dense brownies is enhanced by the sweet, earthy beet purée.

3 squares unsweetened chocolate
½ cup/125 mL unsalted butter
½ cup/125 mL whole-wheat flour
¼ tsp/1 mL salt
½ tsp/2 mL baking powder
¾ cup/175 mL sugar
1 tsp/5 mL vanilla extract
½ cup/125 mL BEET PURÉE ▶
2 large eggs

1 Preheat oven to 325°F/160°C. Line a 9-inch (23-cm) square baking pan with parchment (or spray with oil and dust with flour).

2 In a large saucepan, melt chocolate and butter on low heat, stirring often. Once chocolate has melted, remove from heat and stir in sugar into chocolate until evenly mixed, then add vanilla, beet purée, and eggs. Stir until well mixed.

3 In a small bowl, combine flour, salt, and baking powder. Fold into chocolate mixture, then scrape batter into the prepared pan. Bake for 35 minutes. Cool, then dust with icing sugar, if desired.

PER BROWNIE (2-INCH/5-CM SQUARE): 142 calories, 2 g protein, 9 g total fat, 6 g saturated fat, 42 mg cholesterol, 15 g carbohydrates, 2 g fibre.

BEET PURÉE
Boil two medium unpeeled beets until very tender. Drain, run under cold water to cool, the slip off skins. (Or wrap in foil and roast in 375°F/190°C oven until tender.) Coarsely chop, then whi in a food processor to a smooth purée. This can be refrigerated for 5 days, or frozen up to 3 months.

> BEET IT! MAKES 2

Beets, high in nitrates, can help get you through your next workout. According to one study, nitrates improved oxygen use, helping people exercise for up to 16% longer.

BLEND:
● **4 beets, cooked and peeled**
● **1 lime, juiced ● 2 cups (500 mL) unsweetened coconut water ● 2 cups (500 mL) frozen strawberries**

PER SERVING:
147 calories, 4 g protein, 1 g total fat, 1 g saturated fat, 0 mg cholesterol, 34 g carbohydrates, 8 g fibre.

> SUPERWOMAN SMOOTHIE MAKES 2

Swedish researchers have found that inorganic nitrate—abundant in spinach—results in muscles using less oxygen, which improves muscle performance. Try this naturally sweet smoothie before your workout.

BLEND:
● **2 cups (500 mL) frozen spinach broken into pieces (frozen makes it frothier than fresh) ● 2 bananas ● 1 cup (250 mL) apple juice**

PER SERVING: 147 calories, 4 g protein, 1 g total fat, 1 g saturated fat, 0 mg cholesterol, 34 g carbohydrates, 8 g fibre.

SAVOURY ROSEMARY "SQUAFFLES" MAKES 12

What happens when squash meets waffles? Squaffles—
a flavourful dish ideal for brunch or breakfast-for-dinner.

1 cup/250 mL whole-wheat flour
1 cup/250 mL all-purpose flour
1 ½ tsp/7 mL dried rosemary
1 tsp/5 mL baking powder
1 tsp/5 mL grated lemon zest
¼ tsp/1 mL each salt, ground black pepper
2 large eggs
1 ¾ cups/425 mL buttermilk
¾ cup/175 mL BUTTERNUT PURÉE ▶
¼ cup/60 mL olive oil
1 tbsp/15 mL brown sugar
Maple syrup, optional

SQUASH PURÉE

Peel a squash, cut into cubes, and boil or steam until tender. (Or make a few slashes in a whole unpeeled squash, microwave until tender, then scoop out flesh.) Whirl in a food processor until very smooth. Freeze extra for future squaffle days.

1 Set oven to warm. Heat waffle iron and spray lightly with vegetable oil (skip if silicone-lined).

2 In a large bowl, whisk flours with rosemary, baking powder, lemon zest, salt, and pepper.

3 In a medium bowl, whisk eggs with milk, squash, oil, and brown sugar. Pour over the flour mixture. Gently whisk until just moistened—a few lumps are okay.

4 Depending on make of waffle iron, measure ½ cup (125 mL) batter per waffle and cook until golden brown, about 4 minutes. Keep squaffles warm in oven while cooking remainder of batter. For a sweet touch, serve with warmed maple syrup, if desired.

PER SQUAFFLE: 148 calories, 5 g protein, 6 g total fat, 1 g saturated fat, 37 mg cholesterol, 20 g carbohydrates, 2 g fibre.

CARROT CONFITURE MAKES 2 JARS

This carrot jam is delicious on toast. Try it in place of butter or fruit jam, or on top of light cream cheese.

8 carrots, peeled and sliced
2 cups/500 mL sugar
Zest from one lemon
Juice from two lemons
10 whole amonds, finely chopped

1 Put carrots in a saucepan and fill with water until carrots are covered. Boil until very soft, then purée the carrots.

2 Pour puréed mixture back into saucepan and stir in sugar. Add lemon zest and juice, and bring to a boil. Cook, stirring occasionally, until glassy and the consistency of jam. Remove from heat and stir in chopped almonds.

3 In a medium bowl, whisk eggs with milk, squash, oil, and brown sugar. Pour over the flour mixture. Let cool; transfer to a 2-quart (2 L) jar (or divide into two 1 quart/ 1 L jars) and store in fridge for up to one month.

PER SERVING (2 TBSP/30 ML): 39 calories, 0 g protein, 0 g total fat, 0 g cholesterol, 10 g carbohydrates, 0 g fibre.

INDEX

S

Salad dressings. *See also* Vinaigrette
  amount to add, 67
  basil buttermilk, 67
  chili lime, 67
  cream cheese, 42
  creamy, 45, 48
  curry, 66
  French, hold-the-oil, 67
  fruit, spicy, 47
  honey mustard, 67
  lemon, 52
  lemon and basil, 64
  lime, 60
  mint and honey, 58, 64
  orange, fresh, 66
  orange-sesame, 189
  paprika sour cream, 64
  raspberry nut, 65
  raspberry vinegar, 65
  roasted garlic-buttermilk ranch, 64
  Swap & Drop, 65, 140
  tahini (sesame paste), 55
  wasabi-miso, 66
  yogurt, 65
Salad(s)
  Asian bean sprout, 47
  beef, with mustard vinaigrette, 145
  berry, with passion fruit, 24
  broad bean (fava), 48
  carrot, 101
  chicken, with fruit, 164
  chicken, with ginger, 161, 164
  coleslaw, no-mayonnaise creamy, 211
  coleslaw, with Thai-style beef sandwich, 99
  crab and avocado, 60
  cucumber, radish and snow pea, 202
  Eastern, 44
  egg and radish, 42
  fattoush, with tuna (Eastern salad), 44
  gado gado (Indonesian), 50
  halibut, Asian-style, 63
  Jamaican chicken, 56
  lobster, with lime dressing, 60
  Mediterranean, with edamame, 40
  Mediterranean-style vegetable, 44
  pasta, garden, 45
  pasta and tuna, 39
  pear and gorgonzola, 52
  penne rigati with sesame-orange dressing, 189
  pork, sesame, and noodle, 150
  pork fillet, 145
  rice, with pineapple, spicy, 41
  root vegetable, 49
  salmon, grilled, 63
  shrimp, melon and mango, 58
  Swap & Drop, 60
  tarragon chicken, 55
  tuna, red cabbage, green bean and caper, 61
  tuna, warm Mediterranean, 173
  watermelon and feta cheese, 52
Salmon
  baked, with avocado salsa, 177
  grilled salmon salad, 63
  with honey and mustard, 177
  nutrients in, 120
  PMS symptoms and, 120
  sandwich, grilled, in ciabatta, 91
  seafood jambalaya, 171
  seafood with watercress dressing, 182
  smoked salmon and fresh dill potato skins, 135
  smoked salmon canapés, 122, 147
Salsa
  avocado, 177
  easy, 114
  pepper, shrimp with, 185
  red-hot tomato, 94
  and shrimp tacos, 86
  swaps for dressings, 65
  swaps for sauces, 36
  swordfish with, 173
  turkey and black bean enchiladas, 166
Salt
  substitutes, health concerns about, 217
  Swap & Drop, 37

Sambal oelek, (chili paste), 47
Sandwich(es). *See also* Toast(s)
  bagels, veggie and turkey, grilled, 100
  breakfast, 17
  chicken, avocado and alfalfa club, 83
  chicken salad, curried, 100
  eggplant and tomato, grilled, 78
  hummus and tabouleh, 92
  salmon, grilled, in ciabatta, 91
  Swap & Drop, 88, 100
  Thai-style beef, 99
  tuna, grilled, with tomato and ginger relish, 91
  tuna and carrot on rye, 101
Sardine and pepper toasts, 82
Sauces. *See also* Dessert sauces and toppings; Salad dressings
  blueberry topping for fish, chicken, tofu, 235
  coconut curry, 181
  cucumber, for baked trout, 172
  maple, pear and blackberry, for waffles, 18–19
  peanut, 50
  port, for sirloin steak, 148
  red wine, for sirloin steak, 148
  soy ginger dipping sauce, 167
  watercress dressing, for seafood, 182
Sausages, chorizo, in sausage, pepper and tomato bruschetta, 80
Scallops
  Kung Pao, 162
  nutrients in, 179
  seafood with watercress dressing, 182
Scone(s)
  parmesan and herb drop scones, 25
  tomato, 206
Screwdriver, 131
Seafood. *See also* Fish; Shellfish
  chowder, 77
  jambalaya, 171
  seafood, melon and mango salad, 58
  serving size, 143, 178–9

stew, Italian, 175
  Swap & Drop, 175
  with watercress dressing, 182
Serving size. *See* Portion checker; Portion control
Sesame seed(s)
  allergies to, 92
  calcium in, 120
  -orange dressing, on penne rigati, 189
  PMS symptoms and, 120
  sesame shrimp and crab toasts, 127
  tahini (sesame paste), 55
Shellfish. *See also* Crab(meat); Mussels; Scallops; Shrimp
  lobster salad with lime dressing, 60
  nutrients in, 126, 178–9
  oysters, 126, 178
  scallops, 162, 182
  seafood chowder, 77
  seafood stew, Italian, 175
  serving sizes, 178–9
Shrimp
  chowder, Manhattan, 77
  five-spice, and water chestnut toast, 127
  gumbo, 175
  Kung Pao, 162
  mint and honey dressing or marinade, 64
  nutrients in, 126, 178, 185
  with pepper salsa, 185
  Provençal, 174
  and salsa tacos, 86
  seafood jambalaya, 171
  sesame shrimp and crab toasts, 127
  shrimp, melon and mango salad, 58
  source of iron, 126
  yogurt dressing for, 65
Sleep and appetite, 141, 147
Smoothies and shakes
  banana-mango, 22
  beet-strawberry, 246
  holiday, alternative to eggnog, 147
  smoothie fruit pops, 161
  spinach-banana (Superwoman), 246
  strawberry and yogurt, 22